Deadlands Dime Novel #7

Forbidden God

Fiction & Adventure by: Tim Brown

Editing & Layout: Barry Doyle & Matt Forbeck
Cover Art: Bryon Wackwitz
Logo: Ron Spencer
Interior Art: Paul Daly, Tom Fowler, Ashe Marler, Andy Park & Loston Wallace
Cover Design: Hal Mangold
Maps: Barry Doyle

Pinnacle Entertainment Group, Inc.
P.O. Box 10908
Blacksburg, VA 24062-0908
www.peginc.com or deadlands@aol.com
(800) 214-5645 (orders only)

Printed in Canada.

Visit our website at **www.peginc.com** for regular free updates.

Deadlands: The Weird West created by Shane Lacy Hensley.

Forbidden God

Chapter One

"What are you, sick or something?" The prostitute stepped back from the bed and drew the blanket up to her chin to hide her naked body. The candlelight danced off the brass bed rails and copious mirrors around the tiny room and sparkled in her thick, glittery makeup. Her jaw dropped as her wide eyes wandered across the gunslinger's prone body.

"I told you, no lights!" Ronan pulled the sheets over himself and reached over to pinch out the flame. The sound of distant conversations and squeaking bed springs penetrated the small room, the familiar sounds of a joyhouse on a busy Saturday night. The whore's store-bought perfume mingled with the stench of sweat and cigar smoke from previous customers. Together the odors wafted up through the gunslinger's nostrils, but he had certainly smelled worse.

"Before we get started, there's something you should know. The owner don't allow it, doin' it in the dark, that is. Doesn't want nothin' to get stolen. You're all gray and such. You want a doctor or something?" The whore's brown curls shook as the girl began to tremble, and Ronan knew that she was starting to get the idea she was just about to bed with something strange.

"Now, don't panic," he started, but it was too late, and the young girl's scream split the night. Tears welled in her wide eyes that turned her thick mascara to black mud running down her rouge-covered cheeks. Her shrill wailing still rattled the chandeliers when Ronan heard angry shouts from disturbed patrons and the sound of heavy boots coming up the stairs fast.

"What the hell is going on?" came a voice from beyond the door, and the girl screamed again, backing herself into a corner and covering her face. First came one kick, and then another that broke the door open wide, and in came the white-shirted bartender, leveling a shotgun. "Where is the son of a bitch?"

But in the time it took the barkeep's eyes to adjust to the dim light and pick out his target, Ronan had rolled off the bed, grabbed his blue-steel Colt revolver from its holster hanging from the night stand and put three slugs into his belly. Dead but still standing, the bloodied man managed to pull the trigger on his way down, blasting a lamp and mirror and sending shards of glass everywhere. Ronan grabbed his things and tossed a wad of bills to scatter over the cringing prostitute, then smashed his way through the window and into the cold Salt Lake City night.

Chapter Two

What the hell does a dead man do with his money, anyway? Ronan Lynch had recently spent many a night pondering that one. He still loved getting cash and would gun down anyone who stole it or swindled him out of it. The clink of coins in his saddle bags still gave him a good feeling, just like an empty wallet still made him edgy. But just why he still had a living man's lust for money, he didn't know. It was a strange feeling, and Ronan didn't understand it one bit.

So Ronan tossed coins across the table to consume the things he had in life. He spent money on rooms even though he could just as easily spend the night out with the sage and coyotes. He dropped cash on meals and drinks, though the food tended to rot in his belly and make him belch noxious fumes now and then. Whiskey still had its charms, though, burning down into his dead hulk. But even that was losing its appeal. That didn't stop him from drinking it though.

In dark taverns, he sat across from the living or watched them with narrowed eyes as they enjoyed their meals and their wealth. More and more he loathed the company of living men, just as they probably loathed his kind. Fair is fair, he thought, and he laughed to himself.

Women were another story. The single greatest drain on a living man's funds—pretty women—still drew him in. The sensations weren't quite the same as he remembered, but he craved the touch of flesh-and-blood women, even in death. He was perennially disappointed when, try as he might, he just could not perform the deed any longer, no matter how pretty the girl. More often than not a visit with sporting women ended in screams and gunshots, but that didn't keep him away for long. One thing was clear to him now, that lust is something a man carries with him to the grave.

Ronan ducked through back alleys and along quiet, deserted streets after the trouble at the brothel. Just another shoot-out in a saloon, he thought. Shouldn't draw too much attention here in Salt Lake City. The streets were always bustling with teams pulling lumber or workers, and every day there were new streets on the edge of town. Mud streets, to be sure, but streets nonetheless. Of course, with new construction came a lot of people and garbage, and the flies swarmed around it in black clouds, especially on hot days. Ronan learned not to get too close, since they liked to swarm his dead body and crawl through his clothing if they got the chance.

He ambled his way back slowly toward populated streets, past taverns full of rowdy miners and dance halls full to bursting with liquored-up cowboys. Singing, foot-stomping, dancing, yelling, and smashing glasses, Ronan could hear it all. He moved through the crowds silently and unnoticed until he reached his horse hitched right where he left it. He tipped his hat low over his eyes and quietly mounted, and as he grabbed the reins he found a paper tied there with a red ribbon.

"Watch it, mister!" a passerby shouted when the dead gunslinger's horse ambled too close. Ronan walked his mount down the road while he untied the stiff paper.

"McClellan's Electric Stage," he muttered to himself. It was an advertisement for some kind of magical stagecoach across the salt flats west of the city. "No people there. Sounds kind of nice." He looked around and saw a bunch more flyers just like his, stuffed into windows and door frames, even under saddles. But none of them had a personal message written on the back side like his, he reckoned.

"Meet me at the Douglas Saloon, 12:30 sharp." It was scrawled with a quill and signed by Professor McClellan. Ronan stuffed the paper in his poncho and pulled out a cigarillo, lighting it and taking a puff all in one well-practiced motion. The smoke swirled in his dead lungs and head.

"Civilization is getting a bit too close for me," he said to himself and spurred his animal on toward a darker part of town.

Chapter Three

The morning passed slowly, like they mostly did these days. Sleep eluded him as he lay next to his horse in a deserted alley. Rats and bugs crawled over him freely during the night, but he didn't much care, so long as they didn't linger long or take a nibble. When workmen arrived to paint a nearby storefront Ronan gathered his things and wandered the streets, guiding his mount toward wherever the crowds were the thinnest. By an hour after sunup, though, the whole of Salt Lake City was in the streets and on the move.

Ronan asked a local boy where to find the Douglas Saloon. It was on a street he was familiar with. He avoided a direct route but still got there a couple of hours early. He ordered a drink and nursed it slowly, biding his time until the Professor arrived.

* * *

"So, who told you about me?" Ronan kicked back in his chair, puffing on his cigarillo as the lunchtime crowd ambled through the saloon. The man across from him was the famous Professor McClellan. He'd come in earlier with a bunch of ass-kissers hanging around, but when he saw the undead gunslinger waiting for his appointment he sent the lot scurrying away. A couple of white-shirted Easterners protested briefly but backed away wide-eyed and slowly when they got a load of Ronan. The bespectacled professor was old and wrinkled, Ronan could tell he was sharp as a tack. This wasn't some book-learned idiot from Back East.

"I heard about you from the local constabulary, Mr. Lynch. You've got quite a reputation." The professor's gray hair brushed his shoulders as he turned, looking from side to side. He had a wild look for a learned man, not like Ronan was used to.

"No one's watching us," Ronan assured, pulling the paper flyer from his poncho and dropping it on the table between them. "So, what did you have in mind?"

"I can see you're a man who likes to get right to business," McClellan said smiling. "Good, then I'll get right to the point. I run the electric stage across the salt flats. Invented the thing, actually. Damnedest thing, the salt. Works like a huge electrical battery if you know how to tap into it. It's better than ghost rock, I tell you, and it's free for the taking. Stage runs itself, too, so no teamsters. Just point the thing and go. Of course, you don't care about that." Ronan feigned interest, but it was difficult. He caught himself not paying much attention to the details, letting his eyes wander the busy tavern and its patrons. The professor loved this science stuff, but what was progress to a dead man?

"Anyway, I'm making a fortune until last week when the stage comes through to the other side with nothing but corpses." The Professor leaned closer and lowered his voice. "Chests opened up, and the hearts ripped right out. Nice Mormon fellow in the dry goods business, and his four wives. A couple of them were damn pretty too. Horrible!" The old inventor shuddered at the memory and lifted his thick glasses over the bridge of his nose to wipe his eyes.

"So we can't figure it out. Nothing lives out there. It's a damn salt flat for Christ's sake! Wasn't nothing stolen off them. He had a wad of bills and $75 in gold coins, and not one of them was touched!" McClellan finished his drink and turned the glass upside down on the table, letting the last drops spill onto the table, between the boards, and onto the plank floor.

"Are you sure you got the right man? Sounds like a job for Pinkertons to me," Ronan spoke up.

"Pinkertons? Hell, those fools would probably charge me a thousand and then just fence the salt flats off and put me out of business. No, I need your sort, the type that's dealt with this kind of, well, weird stuff before. I can pay you good, $25 a day, and I'll give you some gadgets I've been working on that might help you out while you're out on the flats."

Ronan fidgeted in his seat, more out of old habit than any corporeal discomfort.

"Look," the professor continued, "I can't afford to be out of operation too long, you know. You've seen the flyers! There are people lining up to ride that damn electric stage, but they'll be gone quicker than a jackrabbit on a date if we don't get this straightened out! So what do you say?"

The dead gunslinger paused for a moment to finish his smoke and extinguish it against the heel of his boot. "I'll need a couple of men to ride along."

"No problem. So you'll do it?"

People were really pressing into the saloon by this time, brushing up against Ronan and making quite a bit of noise. A pair of fat, grinning businessmen laughed loudly, spitting food everywhere at the table next to them. Ronan glared at a woman who nearly knocked him out of his seat with her petticoats, and he shook his head.

"Yeah, I'll do it. But I want my pay in advance 'cause I won't be coming back through here."

"You have plans further west then?" the professor asked.

"Not exactly," Ronan confessed. "Things are just getting a bit too organized around here."

"I see what you mean." McClellan leaned back in his chair and looked around at the hustle and bustle in the bar and on the street outside. "This must be Purgatory for a man like you, Ronan. A man who lives by his guns and wits must not have much use for all of this."

"No, I don't."

"Well, there's still plenty of wilderness out there for you."

"That's what I'm hoping." Ronan stood and dropped a coin on the table and made his way out of the bar.

Chapter Four

It was just a few hours later that Ronan met the inventor at his stagecoach's station on the edge of town, but in that time the clear day had turned cloudy and a bit colder. A cool, dusty wind kicked up in Ronan's face, and the people of Salt Lake City closed their shutters against the west wind and pulled their hats down tight.

"What the hell is that thing?" the skinnier of the Professor's hired men asked as he stood by McClellan's contraption, running his hand along the steel wheels. The elderly professor had brought two other guns, both nondescript fellows in dusty, brown jackets and pants. Ronan eyed them both up and down when they all arrived. Neither of the hired guns appeared too bright or especially talented, and Ronan figured them both for cowards. Learning their names would be pointless, he figured, so he decided to just call them Shorty and Skinny.

"It's the Electric Stage, you dummy," the professor snapped, whipping out an oil can and squirting a bit here and there, pulling on chains and wires stretched tight between gears and other pieces. To Ronan it looked just like a big metal stage with no hitch for a team. Skinny shook his head and rubbed his whiskered chin.

"Well, I'll be damned," Shorty chimed in. Ronan chuckled to himself, thinking the little gunman shouldn't wish that.

"It works just fine, but it's this other thing I wanted to show you all." The Professor walked out beyond the shelter of the stationhouse and into the open. The edge of Salt Lake City ends abruptly where it meets the salt flats. Houses and buildings of fresh, new lumber pressed right up to the flats where the stationhouse was, but from there west it was nothing but white, salty ground with just a few scrawny bushes as far as the eye can see. The two gunmen held their hats against the steady wind and brought their kerchiefs up to their mouths. Ronan found the harsh conditions kind of refreshing, and it had been some time since he stopped feigning discomfort for the benefit of the living who might be watching him.

"This is my new toy," the professor exclaimed, breaking a great big machine out of a big, black trunk on the edge of the salt. The white-haired McClellan pulled out a few pieces, put them together, and attached some wires here and there until the thing took shape, like some wild Gatling gun on a tripod.

"Here, pound these into the ground." McClellan handed two long steel spikes to the gunmen and pointed to two sledges on the earth. With considerable effort, they pounded the spikes into the ground near the thing, arguing the whole time about who would hold the spike and who would wield the heavy hammer. The professor hooked a long copper wire from the bottom of his invention to each spike.

"This is my lightning gun!" he exclaimed, his eyes wide with excitement, laying an affectionate hand on the barrel.

"Your what?" Shorty was very confused, and Ronan admitted to himself that he was too. The gun resembled a firearm in shape only. It was all knobs and dials and glass tubes, with no barrel or breech. He was not entirely sure which was the business end of the thing.

"Observe!" The professor leapt to action, adjusting things here and turning knobs there until the thing emitted a discernible hum and an occasional crackle of electricity. "It works off the electricity in the salt flats, like the stage. Now, watch that big bush there."

McClellan was being generous. The twiggy bush he referred to was all alone about 30 yards off into the flats. He turned the weapon on its tripod, sending Skinny scurrying behind, and pulled the trigger. A thick arc of white-hot lightning appeared between the gun and the bush with a thunderous snap of electrical power. The flash of light blotted out everything else in view, and it took a moment for even Ronan's undead eyes to bring the world back into view. By then the little bush was no longer a bush. It was nothing but a scorched, smoking hole in the ground.

"Damn!" shouted Shorty, rubbing his eyes. He ran his hand gingerly along his opposite arm, where the tiny hairs were standing on end.

"Oh, I should have told you," McClellan apologized. "Don't look right at it."

"You expect us to take that thing with us?" Ronan asked skeptically.

"Well, yes. You never know what you might run into out there." Ronan noted that Skinny and Shorty gave each other a worried glance at the prospect. The undead gunman was certain that, whatever he ran into out there, he would rather face it with his six-gun than with the professor's lightning toy.

CHAPTER FIVE

"This thing's safe, you say?" Shorty took his seat inside the electric stage. As Ronan climbed in, he saw it was nicely appointed, with plush velvet seats and polished rosewood walls. Fine craftsmen had put this thing together, Ronan was certain. There were extra cushions all over the place, and springs under the seats made for a comfortable ride. He could see how people would like traveling in the professor's electric contraption.

"Of course it's safe, except for whatever's slaughtering people out there." McClellan tinkered beneath the thing with a wrench while the men got settled.

"Do you think we should take that damned lightning gun with us?" Skinny wondered, scratching his chin and keeping his voice below where the Professor might hear it.

"Seems like it might kill us if we even set the thing up!" Shorty whispered in agreement. "And what exactly does he mean by 'what we might run into out there'?"

"Beats me, but there ain't no harm taking the thing along with us. We don't have to use it."

They talked it over and decided to take the electric stage out onto the flats, since that gave them the best chance of running into the same bandits that cut up those poor Mormons. Skinny and Shorty were sure they were bandits, anyway, though Ronan doubted it was anything so mundane. Bandits take watches and gold, not hearts. Anyway, the stage was already headed where they needed to go, so all three adventurers hitched their horses to the back of it and lashed their gear on top.

"This thing's like a Kansas City hotel room inside!" Skinny exclaimed, taking his hat off as he got in.

"That's for sure," Shorty agreed, but he didn't bother to take his boots off when he stretched his legs over to rest in the seat across from him. The professor emerged from beneath the mechanical monstrosity and peered in the window. He was covered in grease, oil, and dust from head to foot.

"You don't have to steer the thing, so just sit back and enjoy the ride. I'll expect to see you two in a couple of days, but if you decide to skip out on me just remember that I've got lawman friends all around here who'd love to track you down."

"Not to worry, Mr. McClellan," Shorty reassured him. "We'll report back and expect to get paid on the spot."

"As for you, Mr. Lynch," the old man continued. "Good luck, and thanks for your help." The dead gunslinger nodded in response. He admired the old professor, though he was not exactly sure why. The world of books and screwball gadgets was not for him, but he figured someone had to do it.

Outside the stage, the professor threw a switch, and the thing lurched into motion. Ronan heard the crackle of electricity and the groan of gears turning hard against the wheels. It picked up speed from just a crawl to walking speed to a solid trot. As it did, the ride got a bit rougher but not too bad. Ronan looked back out the window to see the white-haired McClellan waving through the cloud of salty dust kicked up by his beloved contraption.

"Yee-ha! This thing's like a train car with no tracks," observed Shorty. He had put his window down and let in a cloud of salt that settled on the occupants and the velvet seats.

"Put that thing up, you idiot!" Skinny insisted. "This thing is kind of a hoot, ain't it, mister?"

"I ain't one for jawin' too much," Ronan responded without looking up.

"Or for bathing, neither, from the smell of you!" Shorty shot back, and Skinny chortled with him. Ronan figured he did not want to kill them before they helped him find whatever was out on the salt flats. He just patted the wad of money McClellan had given him, now stashed safely in his shirt, pushed his hat down over his eyes, and enjoyed the smooth ride of the professor's electric stagecoach.

Chapter Six

"Look at your hair!" Shorty pointed and laughed at his skinnier counterpart, slapping his thigh uncontrollably. He opened his mouth wide enough to show where teeth were missing or rotten and black.

"What?" Skinny took off his hat and tried in vain to look up past his eyebrows.

"Your hair's sticking up like a paint brush!" The short gunman belly-laughed himself right off onto the stage floor.

"No it ain't!" Skinny insisted, brushing his hand over his hair and beard, not nearly as amused as his partner. He reached over and popped Shorty on the back of the head, but that did nothing to quiet his hysteria.

"You always do this!"

"What?"

"You're always hackin' on me for something!" Skinny made a fist and shook it at his companion.

"Well, then don't do stupid things."

"They ain't stupid things. Not always, anyway."

Ronan tried unsuccessfully to ignore the pair of them, though their banter amused him some. He looked out from beneath the brim of his hat and watched the two horsing around in the stage while the endless white landscape rolled by outside the window. They were heading into the setting sun now, well out onto the endless expanse of lifeless salt flats, many miles from the bustle of Salt Lake. Maybe it was the thrill of riding in Professor McClellan's electric contraption that brought out the children in these two young gunmen. Regardless of the reason, it was funny to watch.

"I hate it when you make fun of me, you moron!" Skinny protested, putting his hat back on his bristly hair. "Like in Abilene when my drawers came unbuttoned that time. Besides, your hair is sticking up, too, you idiot!"

"Is it?" Shorty, who Ronan noticed had numerous scars hiding beneath his scraggly beard, checked his own hair and found it was also sticking up and out from under his hat. When he reached up, he saw the hairs on his arm were dancing, too. "Well, I'll be damned. Look at that!"

"It's this electrical gizmo, I tell you."

"No, it ain't."

"Sure it is, you dumb-ass! What else would it be?" Skinny rubbed his hand through his static-filled hair, then scratched his head. "What about you, cowboy?" The gunman put his leg out and kicked Ronan's feet, but the dead man didn't move. "Your hair's sticking up some, too. That's some scraggly hair you got there, cowboy. All dried out. And your ear's all gray or something. What's your problem, mister."

Shorty chuckled as Skinny leaned over to take a closer look at their companion, but his smile disappeared when Ronan shoved the blue-steel barrel of his Colt revolver right up his left nostril.

"Okay, mister. Okay." Skinny put his hands up slowly and backed away, his eyes narrowed on the gun barrel as he slid his nose back off it. He reached up to rub the gun oil off his nose. Shorty had reached for his sidearm but was smart enough not to draw it out. But even as the man backed away, Ronan could feel both of them eyeing his exposed hand and arm, the dead flesh of his ear and the cold, unliving depth of his eyes. Horror washed over Skinny's face as he sat slowly back in his seat, and he shot a glance at his partner who was equally concerned.

"What the–?"

"Just leave me alone, you bastards, until we've got work to do." And with that Ronan left his living companions to wonder about him, hiding once again beneath his poncho and hat, quietly welcoming the coming sunset. The living are just too damn curious, he decided, and he didn't have the patience for them anymore. Ah well, such is the life of the unliving.

Chapter Seven

McClellan's electrical stage plunged right on into the dark of the moonless night. Skinny and Shorty had put up the windows as the evening air turned chill, but that was about all they dared to do in Ronan's presence. The pair had hardly moved since Ronan had threatened them, sharing only an occasional whisper. Whether they were on to him or not, he didn't know, but either way they didn't like him much. He would have to watch his back. If he had a better idea what they were looking for out on the salt flats, he might have gotten rid of them already, but he thought he might need their guns when the going got tough.

Hours passed as the stage lumbered on over the bumpy trail, the drone of the electric motor mixing with the howling wind. None of them spoke until the steady thrum of the stage's electrical motor crackled unnaturally, lurching the vehicle violently until the thing just shut off and rolled to a stop. The stiff wind on the flats howled against the quiet, metal stage, and the horses tied on behind whinnied restlessly. Ronan instinctively moved his hand closer to his holster and brought all his attention to the lands surrounding the stage.

"Now what?" Skinny exclaimed.

"The damned thing's quit on us, and I sure as hell don't know how to fix it!" Shorty opened the stage door and nearly lost his hat as the wind burst inside. "I'll go take a look at the thing. You check on the horses." He looked quickly over at Ronan and added. "Watch yourself, okay!"

"Right." As Ronan undid his holster and drew out his six-shooter, the pair disappeared out the door. Ronan made his way out into the darkness as well, pulling his hat down against the wind. The flats were dark, and the wind howled hard against his undead body. He scanned the night around him, but there was nothing obvious that would have interfered with the operation of the electric stage, just dusty ground and emptiness.

"Any luck?" he called out to Skinny. The man had lit up a torch and was poking around the various gizmos on the stage. He yanked on a cable and tried to get a couple of gears turning by twisting them with his bare hands, all unsuccessfully. He pinched his finger in one of the gears, yanked it away angrily and stuck the injured digit in his mouth. Skinny looked like a whipped child, and it made Ronan laugh to himself.

"Hell, no. I don't even know how to turn this contraption on!" Shorty kicked the metal wheel and spit on it.

"We'll have to leave it behind and go on with the horses." But Skinny was having a time with them. They were beyond restless now, all three of them pulling hard against their hitches and rearing up to keep the gunman at a distance. Their eyes shined wildly in Shorty's torch. It was the kind of look that some animals got around him these days, Ronan noted.

"What's that?" Ronan cocked his head to one side and drew out his gun.

"What's what?" Shorty started. He turned around slowly, his weapon drawn and pointed out into the darkness.

"That creaking. It's pretty quiet. There, and there again. There must be an old barn or something up ahead of us."

"What, out here on the flats?" Skinny said skeptically. He kept his finger close on the trigger, just in case.

"We'll have to check it out." He opened his revolver and checked its load, and the others did the same. Shorty lit up two more torches, and the three advanced beyond where the stage had mysteriously come to a stop. Every step brought them closer to the sounds of creaking wood and flapping cloth. Skinny stumbled on a worn, gray piece of wood, and Shorty bent low to find an old bit of rope and some metal fittings beneath the light of his torch.

"Jesus Christ! You were right. It is a barn!" The distant edge of the torchlight betrayed a large, wooden structure on the salty ground. The closer they got, the more debris they found on the ground, more wood and corroded metal bits along with rope and canvas. The stuff was not spread evenly on the ground. In some spots, there was quite a bit, while in others there was nothing. Wind had piled sand over most of it. Anyhow, the closer they got to the thing, the less it looked like a barn.

"What the hell is that?" Shorty asked, raising his gun toward the hulk.

Ronan walked in closer. The enormous structure loomed dark before them. The curved timbers, the ropes and canvas, it all added up. "It's a ship."

"You're off your rocker! It can't be a ship!" Skinny looked at Ronan quizzically, but he was smart enough to keep his gun pointing the other direction.

"Hey, I think he's right!" Shorty walked out to the left and close enough that his torch illuminated the bow and the broken masts. The dark, curved timbers were still more or less in place along the great hull of the vessel. "What the hell is a ship doing out here?" The living men looked back at one another and then again at Ronan.

The three stood silently for a few moments, their torches fluttering hard in the wind until Shorty walked over to his companion. "Were you watching close when the old man put together that lightning gun?" he asked. Above them, the star-filled sky was blocked only by the swiftly moving dark clouds and the vast bulk of the bizarre ship.

CHAPTER EIGHT

Shorty and Skinny had stuck their torches in the salty ground to illuminate their work putting together the professor's lightning gun. They pulled out pieces and stuck them in place, then backed up and did it again when they got something wrong. They seemed a little confused by the contraption.

"That piece goes there, dummy!"

"No it don't! I was watching!"

"Shut up, you two!" Ronan insisted, shouting back at the quarrelsome idiots he had been saddled with. They went to their task with some urgency, now unsure of both Ronan and the strange ship they had found in the middle of nowhere.

Ronan walked around the ship as the others worked. There was a lot of junk around, and the whole right side of the thing was smashed pretty good, like it had been thrown down onto the ground. But what was this thing doing here? There was no water about for many miles, and this thing was more like an old sailing ship than a river steamer. It just didn't add up, and the undead gunslinger kept his revolver out just in case. There's comfort to be found in the weight of a good gun in your hand.

"There, I think it's ready." Shorty wiped grease from the gun parts onto his pants.

"Are you going to try it out?" Skinny asked.

"I was sort of hoping you were going to."

"Not me."

"Well, not me either," Shorty shot back. "But, it's humming right, and everything's in place, and we ain't got no pieces left over. It ought to work if we need it."

"If you boys are finished, we probably should check this thing out to make sure it's workin' properly." Ronan ambled up to the pair who turned to make sure he didn't get behind them. The undead gunman knew he could take these two out at any moment, even if they got the drop on him, but he made no threatening moves at all as he approached.

"What, tonight?" Skinny sucked on another pinched finger he had gotten piecing together the lightning gun.

"No time like the present. Besides, it's going to be dark in there day or night I figure. There's a way in through the back of the thing where the hull has split. If there is something in there, it might be a good way to sneak up on it."

The pair fell in right behind Ronan. He figured they were motivated by the payoff McClellan was offering, just like he'd been. He wondered if they might get up the gumption to put some slugs right in his back if things got bad inside the ship. He was willing to bet that wouldn't happen though. The two men needed him too, so they all moved on in toward the ominous, silent ship together.

"You know, it kind of looks like a galleon," Shorty whispered, almost too quietly to hear over the wind.

"A what?" Skinny asked.

"An old Spanish ship. I seen drawings of them when I was a kid, and that's kind of how I remember them. Not smashed and all, but you know what I mean."

Ronan examined the bent and broken timbers as they got closer, and he had no reason to figure Shorty was wrong. The dead gunslinger had never paid much attention to history, but he now wished he had, since at this point it looked like he was going to be around to witness quite a bit of it from now on. As the trio rounded the back of the thing, he brought the two gunmen to the broken section of the hull he'd found earlier. Ancient, dried boards poked out where the ship had been nearly smashed in two pieces, and here and there were spots big enough for a man to crawl into.

"What, in there?" Shorty said in disbelief. "I didn't figure on going in on my belly!" He took a couple of steps back and shook his head.

"You got a better idea?" Ronan glared at him until he backed down.

"Let me see in there," Skinny said, approaching with his torch.

"No!" Ronan shouted, reaching out for the gunman's arm, but not before the torch flames licked up against a protruding board and it burst into flames. "Get back!" The dead man grabbed his hat and beat at the quickly burning plank, but that only spread them faster. Thinking fast, he backed up far enough to kick the hull hard and crack the board right off the ship. It fell to the salty earth and burned away to nothing but ashes in seconds.

"Jesus, this thing's ready to burn!" Skinny smiled. "Might not be a bad idea to put a torch to it, I'd say." He whipped the torch around a bit in the wind and made crackling sounds with his mouth.

Ronan agreed. "Yeah, it crossed my mind too. Let's see how things go inside." And with that, the gunslinger grabbed onto the loose boards and disappeared into the widest opening, crawling on his elbows until his boots disappeared inside of the wreck.

"Leave them damn torches way out there!" he shouted back over his shoulder. "I don't want to be barbecued in here, you know!"

Inside Ronan found nothing but old, broken planks all twisted and poking out every which way. He crawled in between them where he could, snapping them off when possible, but they snagged his clothes to keep him from making much progress. Ten minutes later, he was just far enough inside to let Skinny crawl in behind him, going through the same hole. The light from the torches outside filtered in sufficiently for them to see what they were doing, but only barely, since all the broken boards sent a thousand shadows every which way. The constant creaking of the old ship in the strong wind was much louder inside, forcing them to shout to make themselves heard.

"This whole part of the ship's smashed," Skinny called up to him, but Ronan barely heard his living compatriot. He was imagining what the ship might have been like when it was new, sailing the oceans somewhere far away. He had a clear picture in his mind of bright skies and clear, warm waters. The smell of ocean breezes and island flowers danced in his nostrils. The image was so clear that it took his attention away from the several dark shapes that surrounded him among the broken planking.

"Dammit!" he cried suddenly. "Rats!" Two shaggy rats leapt out of the shadows and right at Ronan's face, one sinking its teeth right into his cheek. He quickly brought his elbow down onto one of them, snapping its back against a sturdy board, but the second was more elusive and vanished back into the shadows, its sharp nails scraping against the rotten planking.

"Jesus Christ! They're huge!" Ronan could not see behind him in the close confines of the collapsed ship, but he heard Skinny beating away rats too. Two scurried past in front of him, but even Ronan's lightning-fast shots failed to hit home. Ronan reached for the first one he'd killed—it was big as a small dog—and found it was still twitching. The rodent was half rotted away, its bones and muscles sticking out here and there, and a fire burned in the tiny creature's eyes that told the gunslinger he was among his own. This thing was undead.

"Throw the ones you kill in back of you, and let Shorty burn them outside!" he called back behind him.

"Do what?"

"Just do it! They're diseased," he lied. Maybe they wouldn't figure it out, he reckoned. He tossed the rat back behind him and kicked it along back to Skinny. As the two worked their way forward they each smashed a couple more and sent them on back out to be roasted too, but not before losing some hide to the elusive, fiendish rats. The going was tough, but in time the various smashed decks of the ship opened up some, and the trio could crawl through more easily. Ronan found a place to sit up and wait, In just five minutes, he shot about a dozen of the hideous rats. Their grinning carcasses nearly crumbled in his grip as he passed them back to Skinny and on to their eventual cremation.

"The way ahead of you clears up," Ronan called back behind him, welcoming the opportunity to stretch out his legs a bit. Even in his present state, he found discomfort from awkward movements, just as he did when he was alive. He took out a cigarillo but refrained from striking a match. The feel of it between his lips and teeth was enough.

"So, there's undead here," he said softly to himself. "This should be interesting." Ronan seemed to actually be comfortable with that thought.

CHAPTER NINE

"Through here." Shorty had joined the others in an open area beyond the worst parts of the wreckage, 15 yards into the smashed ship. The shadows of the planking between them and the torches outside darkened the area considerably, but they could still make their way along pretty well. "There's a large open area in here," Ronan guided the gunmen, certain he could see better in the near darkness than they could. He worked himself down through a split in several large beams and dropped onto the floor. "We can light the lantern down here. Pass it through."

Shorty did what the gunslinger asked, handing through the oil lantern he had gone back to get from the immobile electric stage. Ronan struck a match against his heel and carefully lit the lantern away from any of the nearby timbers, then turned up the flame slowly. For a moment, he saw a wide hold of a ship, filled with barrels of water and wine, crates of pottery, and bag after bag of grain, some being stacked against the walls by dark-skinned men.

Sunlight poured in from above as the men worked, and again the scent of the sea permeated the air. But when Ronan shook his head and looked again, all he saw was the wrecked ship, the ceiling smashed down low. Shorty and Skinny slid down the passage behind him.

"You look like you've seen a ghost," Skinny commented, picking up his hat off the ground where it had fallen from his head.

"No," Ronan collected himself. "There's really nothing here."

"What are these for?" Shorty pointed out iron chains and manacles mounted into the large beams here and there. The metal pieces were obviously old, but in the dry salt flats they had not rusted at all. Ancient blood made dark stains on the cold, metal cuffs.

"Maybe this was a slave ship." Skinny found several piles of cowhides, now brittle and ancient. He tried to pick some up, but they fell to pieces in his hands. "This place gives me the creeps. I don't like it in here. Hey, what's this?" He kicked away some dust on the ground where the glint of shining gold had caught his eye. He bent over and picked up a small handful of golden coins. "Well I'll be a–"

"What was that?" Ronan said, turning to where he heard motion behind the smashed crates of broken pottery. Timbers creaked loudly in the shadows there, and something large banged up against a pile of old crates that immediately toppled towards them.

"Watch it!" An enormous dark shape lunged through the darkness and over the piles of crates, right at the gunmen. It knocked over piles of debris and kicked up enough dust that Ronan couldn't see what it was.

"It's a steer! A great big bastard!" Shorty shouted.

"Son-of-a-bitch!" Skinny unloaded his six-gun right at the beast that rushed through their ranks, nearly hitting Ronan a couple of times as the dead man dove out of the way. Shorty reached for his gun too, but he didn't get off a shot before the huge beast hit him hard and gored him right through the thigh. He screamed and grabbed at the wound as the enormous black steer reared back and flung his body around like a child's doll.

"Emmit!" Skinny drew his other gun and fired into the beast, sending it into a frenzy, spinning and smashing things until it bolted right at the outer hull planking. It smashed straight through, using Shorty's body to take the brunt of the impact. The entire ship shook with the impact, splintering boards and kicking up dust. Light from the torches left outside streamed in through the new opening.

Skinny beat Ronan out through the broken boards and onto the open salt flats again. Shorty was still hanging from the enormous steer's horn, but he was completely limp and bent in all sorts of unnatural ways. Skinny's eyes streamed with tears, and in his rage he threw his empty gun at the monstrous thing. Its black coat was deep as the night, but its eyes glowed red with evil magic. It backed away, shaking its head to free itself of the carcass it carried on its horns, and Skinny saw his chance.

"That son-of-a-bitch is gonna die!" Skinny sprinted for the lightning gun, still standing where they had erected it. The beast watched him go, but it could not free itself of Shorty's body. Having seen McClellan's weapon in action once before, Ronan took off running away from wherever Skinny might aim it.

The huge beast snorted and shook itself violently one last time, finally throwing Shorty's corpse high into the air to land with a sickening thud. It snorted again and dug its heels against the salty ground, growling with rage. It spied Ronan and prepared to charge. Then Skinny switched on the lightning gun with an audible click and electrical hum. The beast tilted its head and lowered its horns to charge it instead as the gunman turned the bizarre weapon toward the beast.

"Die, son-of-a-bitch!" Skinny pulled the trigger and a bright bolt of lightning pierced the dark night, blocking out everything else from view. Ronan heard a shriek of agony from the savage steer and then the sound of sizzling meat. The thunderous roar of the weapon echoed off into the night even after Skinny switched it off, and their eyes adjusted slowly. The beast was still trying to move, but it was nothing but a ruined hunk of burning flesh. Beyond it, though, the gun had hit the ship as well, setting it ablaze in several spots.

"Well," Ronan pointed out, "you got it." Skinny was frozen where he stood by the lightning gun, which was also smoking and ruined. The dead gunfighter walked over to his living companion, and the pair watched the strange ship erupt into towering flames that licked way up into the night sky, illuminating the landscape far around them.

In minutes, the entire vessel was one huge pyre, enveloping the monstrous steer and Shorty's fallen body. The searing heat sent the two men back as far as the stage and horses. They sat there silently as the flames consumed the strange vessel until the first flares of dawn flickered through the thick smoke.

CHAPTER TEN

Ronan built a small fire from the loose timbers lying around just after the sun came up. He put on some coffee and made some biscuits for Skinny. The living man sat with his back against one of the stage wheels, just watching the smoldering pile of ash that had been the strange ship.

The pair had watched the fire into the dawn. Horrid screams of other strange beasts split the air as it burned and collapsed in on itself. Strange flaming critters leapt out and ran out onto the salt flat where they burned and died. The entire grisly episode was surreal, and the light of day made even Ronan wonder if what they had seen and done the night before ever actually happened.

"Coffee?" he asked. Skinny barely acknowledged him, his soot-covered cheeks tracked with tears. "I'm sorry about your friend," he added, but he thought better of elaborating and backed away to his campfire. Ronan knew he didn't have the words, and he didn't want to make the situation any worse. One of his partners was dead, and he needed the other one alive.

"We grew up together, you know," Skinny offered. His innermost thoughts were bubbling to the surface. "Back in Missouri. I told his momma I'd look out for him."

Ronan empathized with the gunman. He had lost a lot of friends in his day, but for him it got easier with time. Ronan had learned to accept death—even his own. He was about to share that with Skinny when the man spoke up again.

"I think I'm going crazy." Ronan could tell he was serious. "I think you're some kind of—Hell, I don't know what you are—some kinda monster, and maybe I am too. I just wish I knew." New tears welled up in his eyes as he spilled his guts, his eyes never wandering from the smoking wreck before them. "God have mercy on my soul!"

Ronan sat and listened carefully, tending his fire slowly, all the while keeping a hand near his Colt and watching his companion's gun hand. You can never be too careful with someone who's telling you he's crazy, Ronan figured, whether he means it or not.

"I've been seeing things. Weird things. Like oceans and ships and such. And I swear to God there were voices in my head last night telling me to—to—to do horrible things." With that Skinny buried his face in his dirty hands and wept uncontrollably. Ronan let him cry it out, wondering about his own visions on the previous night.

"What kind of horrible things?" Ronan asked cautiously.

Skinny hesitated. "To—to cut out your heart. His, too." He looked away, ashamed to admit something so dreadful. He reached into his pocket and pulled out tobacco and papers, but he trembled too much to roll his own. Ronan produced a cigarillo and offered it to his shaken companion.

"Thanks." He lit the smoke off of Ronan's extended match and drew in deeply. "I have no idea what made me think things like that."

"It's this place," Ronan reassured him, moving over to straighten the saddle on his mount, which was still hitched behind the stationary stage.

"You think so?"

"Sure. You heard McClellan. That's why he hired us, 'cause something is cutting out hearts around here. Just keep your wits about you, and you'll be all right." Ronan pretty much believed it as he said it, but he felt safe that nothing would want his withered heart at any rate.

"You think burning up the ship has put an end to all of this mess?" Skinny asked hopefully, wiping the sweat from his brow. The rising sun was already heating things up on the bright-white salt flats.

"I would imagine. But there's still that gold that we should go after."

"Wouldn't it all be melted?"

"Coins or lumps, it's all the same to me." Ronan wasn't about to just leave the gold under the smoldering ship. "It should make a nice split, even if there's just the handful we saw."

"I don't know," Skinny hesitated. "It doesn't seem right with Shorty gone and all."

"Look at it this way: Would you have taken the gold if Shorty was still around?"

"I suppose you're right." The gunman stood up and was visibly feeling much better. He wasn't shaking like he was before, Ronan noted, and he had stopped whimpering. "Thanks for listening to me carry on like that."

"There isn't much else to do out here." Ronan loaded his revolver while Skinny collected himself next to the metal stagecoach.

"Well, are you?" he asked Ronan

"How do you mean?"

"Are you a monster? I'm sorry about all of that, but I really need to know."

Ronan thought for a moment before answering, which probably wasn't the smartest thing to do. "Monster or not," he nearly confessed, "we're working together, aren't we?"

Skinny laughed. "Yeah, I suppose we are." He wiped his grimy hand on his trousers and extended it toward the dead gunfighter. Ronan took it, and they shook hands warmly.

"Earl."

"What?"

"My name's Earl."

Chapter Eleven

The hulk had nearly burned itself out by noon. There were no more open flames, and most of the smoldering wood was now cool ash just blowing away in the steady wind. The pair still had to move carefully, though, since there were plenty of red-hot spots left beneath their boots.

"I think it was over here," Earl pointed out, kicking aside a couple of heavy beams that had not burned through. Ronan couldn't recall exactly where they had seen the gold coins, but he was certainly ready to spend the day looking.

"Dig through to the ground," he suggested. "The heavy gold would have sunk through, I think."

"Makes sense." Whenever the wind picked up, the ash launched into the air in thick clouds, forcing them to look away and cover their mouths. An hour passed without results when Ronan's boot plunged between two piles of ash and deep into the ground.

"Here, look at this." Earl worked his way over as Ronan freed himself and cleared away a large hole in the ground. He grabbed a lump of charcoal and dropped it in to hear it fall. "It's pretty deep, maybe 20 feet."

"What do you think? Should we go down there?" Earl mopped his brow, shaking his head.

"It's probably worth checking out. I'll go alone if you don't want to, but I keep anything I find." Ronan gave him a sly look—he knew that would change his mind. Earl looked at Ronan, then down the hole, and then back at Ronan again.

"No, I'll go with you. We'll need the lantern." The gunman loped off to the stage while Ronan cleared the rest of the ash and charcoal away from the gaping hole. With the aid of the lantern, they could see deeper into the opening in the ground. It sloped away from them at an angle so they could slide down one at a time.

"Hang onto my feet," Ronan insisted, and Earl lowered the dead gunfighter into the hole head first while he crawled down on his elbows. The deeper into the hole, the worse it stank, and Ronan had to keep wiping the salty dust from his face and eyes. He slithered easily down the hole, though, quickly disappearing underground until Earl had to let go of his boots.

"I'm coming in after you," the living man announced, and in minutes they had both dropped into a large chamber dug beneath the ground. Ronan had seen plenty of mine shafts, and this was much more primitive. In the lantern light, he saw that the earthen walls were very unstable, having collapsed in several spots, the ceiling and walls held in place poorly by stacked timbers that had once been cut out of the strange ship they had torched the night before. A couple of tunnels led out of the chamber to either side.

"What the hell was this place?" Skinny asked, using the barrel of his gun to dig a line of dust out of the wall.

"I have no idea, but the fire would have suffocated anything that was alive down here." Of course, Ronan figured that living things would be the least of their problems, since both the rats and steer from the strange ship had been, like him, bereft of life. "Come on."

But when Earl did not quickly follow him, Ronan turned to see him standing still, pallid and shaking, his eyes staring blankly. By the time the Ronan managed to reach his side, Earl's jaw had dropped, and drool was spilling from the corner of his mouth. Ronan didn't know what to think.

"Earl?" he began, but the living man suddenly glared down at him, the lantern light dancing in his wide eyes. The gunman dropped his six-shooter to the dusty floor and reached for Ronan's throat, all the while screaming something in Spanish that the dead gunfighter didn't understand. Ronan defended himself easily, grabbing the deranged gunman by the wrists and sending him flying across the underground chamber. Earl hit the wall with a sickening thud.

Earl collected himself there and drew a Bowie knife from his boot, then jumped up to lunge again when he stopped dead in his tracks. Standing between the two, appearing as if from the dust itself, there was a horrid, ancient dead woman. She twisted her head menacingly to face each gunfighter in turn.

"Leave this place! The Spaniard has your mind!" The voice was dry as the desert, and her language something strange. Ronan had never heard the tongue before, but he understood perfectly nonetheless.

Terror washed over Earl's face, and he turned and ran screaming through one of the tunnels leading away from the chamber. Ronan thought about going after him, but he knew Earl was too far gone.

The horrid woman then turned to Ronan, her once-dark skin now wrinkled and caked with salty dust. Every orifice of her face—her ears, eyes, nostrils, even her mouth—were packed with salt that sprinkled gently down her body with every movement. The creature looked at the undead gunslinger for a moment, then crooked one finger in the direction of a pile of debris in a remote corner on the chamber floor. In the instant that he turned to look, the she-beast vanished just as suddenly as she had appeared.

CHAPTER TWELVE

"April 15, 1559," Ronan read aloud from the ancient manuscript he'd found where the salted woman had pointed. Its pages were brittle and faded, but Ronan read it aloud freely, translating the ancient Spanish text easily despite never being able to read that language before. Its message, he reckoned, must be vital to the salted one's purpose for her to bestow such a magical power upon him. Ronan figured it was the least he could do to actually read the thing.

In the light of his lantern, he read from the ledger of the ancient conquistador Captain Diego de Velasco. The first entry, written somewhere in Mexico, described how the Spaniard traded with an Aztec peasant for a huge golden bowl. "Were the Aztecs granted no wisdom by God?" the conquistador had written. "Why else would one trade a massive golden bowl for a handful of worthless gems?"

Ronan read further, careful to not crumble the tattered edges of the parchment. The Spaniard wrote of his last mission aboard the galleon he hoped would one day take him back to Spain—once his work in the New World was done. "July 12, 1559, on board the galleon *Narvaez*." The ledger listed the contents and passengers for a new colony somewhere, including slaves, soldiers, and horses, sailing on several ships headed by the *Narvaez*, but de Velasco's dreams of personal wealth were still apparent. "The next time I come to Mexico it will be as a conqueror and plunderer! I will have all that I desire."

The writings took a turn toward paranoia shortly after, as the galleon put to sea. De Velasco's tone became increasingly restless and combative as strange, devilish events befell the doomed ship. "Goats and chickens have been found on all the ships, brutally slaughtered. Bloody corpses of slaves are found every morning with their hearts ripped out. There are rumors of devils among the crew, and beasts coming up over the side like serpents in the darkness. An old Tlaxcalan woman's eyes pierce my soul whenever I pass her in the hold. I fear that if her eyes don't burn through my soul first, she will come after me in my dreams. I sleep with my pistols in hand."

Ronan could see the images in his mind very clearly, more clearly than just the Spaniard's ancient text could muster. Savagely murdered slaves, the corpses butchered. The fear. The hatred. He read on.

"Today a black slave didn't get to his feet when I ordered it, so I ran him through." Ronan saw it happen, the blade protruding from the helplessly chained slave's shoulders, the smell of his blood as it spilled out onto the ground. "They glared at me wide eyed as I dragged the corpse below decks, but they don't understand. In my cabin, I laid the dead man on top of the idol to bleed into the bowl. I broke it out of the crate days ago and keep it in the center of the room. Coutzlatl they called it, the Forbidden God! It's beautiful. At night, I dream of it!"

Ronan closed the book as images of feathered gods and bloody rituals filled his head to bursting. Grotesque piles of corpses and maggots, the taste of gore in his mouth, and the screaming of children ringing in his ears all competed to dominate his mind. The righteous slaughter and offerings of blood nearly choked him. But the pages beckoned him back, and he continued to read.

"September 15, 1559," he muttered, the last entry. "Coutzlatl speaks to me every day now. I have not heard God in weeks. Does one block the others' words, or are they one in the same? The ship is all but abandoned, and the other ships have been gone for days. We float now with heavy weather approaching." The storm raged in Ronan's ears, the waves crashing, and the wind churning gray seas.

"The stench of rotting corpses sickened me at first, but now I drink it in. They are stacked in the corridor and on the deck, their hearts heaped in Coutzlatl's bowl, buzzing with flies and cockroaches. The old Tlaxcalan woman eludes me though. She is a medicine woman of some sort, or so one of her kind blurted out when pleading for his life. She cannot escape me for long!" The salt woman: the Tlaxcalan witch doctor and the Spaniard's nemesis. It was her, Ronan was certain.

"The seas are heaving, and the sails are shredded. The timbers creak as the waves crash over the deck. We're taking on water. Coutzlatl forgive me!"

The Spaniard's last entry rang in Ronan's ears as if he had heard it screamed rather than just read it. De Velasco's bloody final days, his descent into savage madness driven by the magical golden bowl of the ancient forbidden god, all these things were ingrained on Ronan's mind.

"Why tell me all this?" He called out in the underground chamber, standing and letting the ancient text slip to the dusty floor. "Why me?" He grabbed his head and struggled against the terrible images in his mind, of butchered children and still-pumping hearts, and he realized that his thoughts and words were no longer in English, but in the long-forgotten language of the Tlaxcalan.

CHAPTER THIRTEEN

Ronan was not certain how long he had wandered or to where. The tunnels and subsequent chambers of the primitive underground were much like where he had read the ancient text, filled with dry timbers from the galleon and salty dust of the flats. Thoughts of three-centuries-old atrocities faded slowly, only to be replaced by more immediate thoughts of life without life. Ronan had not pondered the depressing notion of prolonged undeath until now. The image of the withered Tlaxcalan witch doctor haunted him as he staggered through the dust-filled chambers. Was he doomed to madness? Would he inevitably turn into a savage murderer like the Spaniard de Velasco? Scenario after scenario raced through his mind while he walked through the endless tunnels, none of them with happy endings. The unending expanse of time before him loomed large and frightening. Eternity beckoned.

At first he thought the voices he heard were in his head, either past victims or future tormentors come to harass him in his moment of weakness. But they were real and brought his attention back to the world. Shouts and screams echoed down the tunnel before him, and Ronan leapt to action. He drew his Colt in one swift motion and ran stealthily toward the sound of angry Spanish voices.

As Ronan rounded a corner, three undead soldiers dressed in conquistador armor emerged from the ink-black darkness. Ronan skidded in the dust as they hissed at him. One of the zombies stepped toward Ronan, and he put a bullet square between its eyes. The undead warrior dropped to the earth, once again lifeless. The other two hesitated, then stumbled toward the gunslinger again. Two more shots rang out, and one zombie fell to the floor, while the other smacked against the wall, its skull shattering open upon impact. Ronan nodded his head at the creatures, and blew the smoke off the end of his barrel.

"You fellas need a little more brains when it comes to picking yer battles. This time you messed with the wrong dead guy," Ronan said as he once again made his way toward the voices.

* * *

Ronan burst into a large chamber to find Earl, dust-covered and slump-shouldered from exhaustion, confronted by a grinning, black-skinned figure. The creature leaned in toward Earl with its arm outstretched, its sword resting firmly against Earl's neck.

"De Velasco!" Ronan shouted suddenly. The creature was drawn, its skin blackened and shrunk down on its bones. It still wore the rusted helm and breastplate it did in life. The creature turned briefly to look upon the intruder, taking the point of its long rapier away from Earl's throat temporarily. It looked upon Ronan with empty, black sockets and hissed loudly between its yellow, broken teeth.

"Run, Earl!" Ronan's warning came too late, and in one well-practiced motion the black-skinned abomination turned and drove the point of his long, thin blade deep into Skinny's chest. Earl jerked and choked in agonizing pain, and Ronan raised his pistol and pointed it at the undead captain. The snapping and ripping of bone and sinew followed as the blade circled the man's sternum and plucked his living heart from his chest in a sickening spray of crimson gore.

"No!" Ronan shouted and fired simultaneously. Earl's lifeless body crumpled to the floor as Ronan's bullet rang off the Spaniard's breastplate. The concussion of the bullet being fired in the tight chamber shook loose a cloud of dust from the walls and ceiling that clouded the entire room in an instant. Ronan fired twice more, further obscuring the room. "Damn!"

He peered through the slowly settling dust and quietly circled to his left, ready to blast holes in the cruel undead beast the moment he saw it. But the creature's blade shot through the dust cloud faster than he could react, flicking the Colt from his hand. Ronan could not see where it fell, and he quickly drew his knife from his belt. In a moment, the dust thinned enough that he could see, but his missing gun and his armored opponent eluded him.

"De Velasco, your end is near!" he said, again in Tlaxcalan. Was the witch doctor living through him now? A powerful, bony hand grabbed him around the mouth from behind and nearly tore Ronan's head off his neck. He turned and drove his blade against the rusted breastplate in a shower of sparks. The two grappled and punched until Ronan was face to face with the grinning Spaniard. Worms and bugs crawled freely along its thin lips and cheeks as it laughed horridly.

Unable to get a good grip on the monster's body, Ronan grabbed the bottom of the breastplate and lifted with all his might, the leverage helping him break its grip on his body and dump the beast on the dusty ground. One thing was certain. His more ancient opponent was much stronger, and Ronan doubted he could survive a long fight.

"Where's my damn gun?" he shouted, but the beast leapt at him again and knocked him completely off his feet. It crushed him to the ground, digging its bony nails into his shoulder and ribs. Ronan struggled against the stronger creature, trying to free an arm or leg, but it held him fast. In an instant, it grabbed his throat, tearing at his undead flesh, trying to rip his head off his shoulders. Sinew snapped, dead muscle tore, and Ronan knew his end was near.

A shot rang out, and the beast's rusted helmet flew off its head with a bang. A second shot hit the back of its head, blowing a big chunk of dusty, dried brains all over Ronan's face. The stunned beast loosened its grip slightly, and Ronan seized his opportunity.

He rolled the brainless creature onto the floor, and in one motion he grabbed up its iron helmet and smashed it down like a club. He beat the Spaniard's head to a ruin, then crushed every bone and joint in its still-twitching body. Its chest crushed, knees and elbows cracked, and virtually every bone pulverized, de Velasco's undead corpse wriggled harmlessly on the dusty ground. But like him, it couldn't die.

"Well, I guess I ain't much surprised to see you now." The salt-encrusted corpse of the unarmed witch doctor stood before him, silent and grim, but Ronan fought to speak only in English rather than the strange language that she had put in his head. "Your dirty work's done. 'Course, it'll probably put itself back together before long and be right back in business, just like in one of them cheap novels they print Back East!" He chuckled at the thought, but the undead Indian woman didn't respond. She continued to stare at him through those distant eyes.

"Truth is, all your ancient curses and nonsense don't mean crap to me, lady. You made me help you, 'cause if you hadn't I probably wouldn't have. Truth is, I'd rather stick my neck out for a man like poor dead Earl here than risk a fingernail for a thousand of you old, dead bastards!"

Ronan gathered up his missing Colt from the underground chamber's dusty floor. Across the room, he found Earl, his stone-dead hand gripping his own revolver, still smoking from the two rounds he'd put into the back of the undead Spaniard's head. Ronan grabbed the gun by the barrel and put it in his belt, then hoisted the dead man over his shoulder and made his way back to the surface.

Chapter Fourteen

Ronan buried Earl and Emmit side by side in the windswept Utah salt flats. Strangely enough, he missed their jovial camaraderie. The poor suckers had traded their lives for a few dollars, and that thought somehow made him sad. Maybe he wasn't completely dead after all.

After a while, Ronan figured out how to turn the stage around and get it started again for Salt Lake City. He wrote a quick note to the Professor explaining what he knew and what had happened. He apologized for not doing any more, and he enclosed the money the professor had given him.

Ronan put the cash and the letter in the stage and sent it on its way. He had paid just enough attention to know how to turn the thing on. The stage clanked along to the east, homing in on Salt Lake City, back to where it might be useful again.

Actually, he wasn't sure if there was danger left here or not. He figured the weird ship had caused the contraption to shut off in the first place, and now that the galleon was a smoking ruin the electric stage worked just fine. It didn't make much sense to Ronan to let McClellan risk more lives to find out though.

There was gold to be found here, maybe even the golden bowl, but he would not succumb to its madness. The thought of it made him wince. No one was going to find him running around insane somewhere in a few hundred years. No gunman in the future was going to come after him as if he was some monster protecting its hoard. He figured eternity wouldn't grab hold of his mind unless he let it. The future was starting to scare him a little, but he decided he wanted to scare it instead. Let some other fool make a try for the golden bowl. Good luck to him too. Ronan figured he had enough gold for now.

He tied his comrades' horses on behind his own and headed west. The animals were greatly relieved now that the ship was gone, which was another good sign that things were safe out here again. There was plenty of gear for him to choose from, so Ronan saddled up with everything he could carry, but he left the ruin of McClellan's lightning gun where his partners had set it up. That thing seemed too dangerous for Ronan to even consider disassembling it for the stage's return trip. If McClellan wanted it bad enough, he figured he would come get it.

OSTON

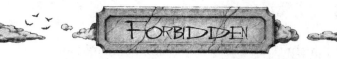

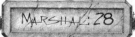

Forbidden God

The Adventure

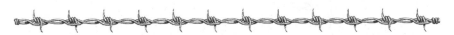

The Story So Far

The heroes are hired by Professor Cyrus McClellan to investigate mysterious murders on his electric stagecoaches across the Great Salt Flats. They take the bizarre stage, along with several other of the professor's inventions, to the center of the flats where they find the wreckage of a large sailing ship, an ancient Spanish galleon, almost 1,000 miles from any ocean. They investigate to find that the ship was hurled here 300 years ago from the Caribbean by a magically induced hurricane called to banish an evil Aztec idol to the isolation of the lifeless salt flats.

The professor's passengers have reawakened the idol that has rested here quietly for three centuries, and the characters must now confront its magic and undead minions.

There are two powerful undead beings left wandering the galleon. The first is the Spanish Captain de Velasco. The second is Pohqui, the Tlaxcalan medicine woman who summoned the magical hurricane. These two dominate the site, invading the minds of the heroes as they penetrate deeper into the underground beneath the wreck.

The *Forbidden God* is designed for three to five heroes with at least one huckster. Having at least one adventurer that speaks and reads Spanish is a plus.

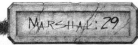

The Setup

The paper flyers are spread out all over town. They read: "Cross the Salt Flats in just One Hour, in the comfort of McClellan's Amazing Electric Stage." You can see them everywhere you look—floating through the streets with the breeze, stuck under saddles on hitched horses, slid under hotel doors, even left on bars and restaurant tables. No place in the town is safe from the aggressive advertising barrage. This McClellan's a go-getter, that's for sure—or he's a desperate man who really needs the business.

Of course, the one the heroes get is special delivered with a message scrawled on the front of the flyer—"Meet me at the Douglas Saloon, 12:30 sharp"—and signed by the entrepreneur himself.

By 1:00, the man hasn't shown, and the heroes should be ready to leave. Just then, a group of people swing the doors wide, all jabbering and carrying on. In front's McClellan—the conversation whirls around him—followed by a couple of businessmen in suits with gold-chained pocketwatches, and a reporter with an open notepad, all talking to him at once.

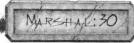

"We'll talk about that in the morning. Get the bankers over there too. No, I ain't related to that yellow-belly! Why does everyone ask me that!" McClellan stops and spots the heroes sitting at your table and turns to his companions. "Now, if you'll excuse me, I'm late for some business with these gentlemen. Good day to you!" He hurries them all back out into the street and comes quickly over to the heroes' table.

"I hope I can count on your discretion," he says quietly, stroking his beard and motioning the barmaid for a drink. "We've got a world of trouble." The aging inventor shakes his long hair out of his face, flips a coin onto the table and collects his thoughts.

"I'll get right to the point. I run the electric stage across the salt flats. Invented the thing, actually. Damnedest thing, the salt. Works like a huge electrical battery if you know how to tap into it. It's better than ghost rock, I tell ya, and it's free for the taking! Stage runs itself, too, so no teamsters. Just point it and go! Of course, you boys don't care about that."

"Anyway, I was making a fortune until last week when the stage came through to Ackensack with nothing but corpses." He leans closer and lowers his voice further.

"Chests opened up, and the hearts ripped right out. Nice Mormon fellow who was makin' a decent living in the dry-goods business. His four wives also died with him. Couple of them were pretty too. It's a damn shame—in fact it's downright horrible!" The old inventor shudders at the memory and lifts his thick glasses over the bridge of his nose to wipe his eyes.

"So we can't figure it out. Nothing lives out there. It's a damn salt flat for Christ's sake! Wasn't nothing stolen off them. He had a wad of bills and $75 in gold coins, and not one of them was touched!" McClellan finishes his drink and turns the glass upside-down on the table.

"I can't talk to the Pinkertons. Those fools would charge me a thousand and then just fence the salt flats off, put me out of business. No, I need folks who've dealt with this kind of, well, weird stuff before. I can pay you good, $25 a day each, and give you some gadgets I've been working on that might help you out.

"I can't afford to be out of operation too long, you know. You've seen the flyers! There's people lining up to ride that damn electric stage, but they'll be gone quicker than a jackrabbit on a date if we don't get this straightened out! So, what do you say?"

The Professor's Toys

The Great Salt Flat is a wide expanse of God-forsaken wilderness to the west and north of Salt Lake City. The flats flood sometimes when too much rain drains down into the big lake, but that hasn't happened since the Reckoning.

The ground is saturated with salt, and it looks like a huge floor of cracked adobe for about 20 miles in all directions. No plants can grow in all the salt, of course, and that keeps pretty much everything else away except some salt rattlers and the occasional scorpion.

Professor McClellan is as good as his word if the heroes accept his offer. He provides them with everything he has promised, and if they finish the job he sticks to his word for the payment. His next stage leaves at 4:00 in the afternoon, bound straight across the salt flats for Ackensack, and the heroes should be the only people on it.

If the heroes don't want to take the stage, they can get horses and such and pack out there the hard way. Either way, the Professor shows up with some advice and other equipment before they take off.

Chapter One: McClellan's Electric Stage Stop

The stop is way out on the edge of Salt Lake City, where the town's growing fast. The saloons and stables flank mud streets crisscrossed with planks to keep folks' feet dry. Teams pull wagons of lumber and barrels through the deep mud while gunslingers and saloon girls hurry here and there in the bustling pace of the city.

The station itself is right on the edge of the flats, and there aren't any more buildings beyond it. A big sign overhead says "From here to Ackensack before your next meal!" Someone's scrawled in chalk "Next stage leaving 4:00" under that. It's a primitive setup, with a few planks for a floor, and a bent awning to keep most of the rain off the heads of waiting passengers.

Next to the platform is the small, one-man ticket-booth. Passengers wait anxiously in line at the booth, ready to purchase tickets. A black-vested fellow who normally takes the money for the tickets stands behind a crude barred window, but instead of taking money he's making apologies.

"There ain't no stage today, I'm sorry," he tells an angry throng waving tickets or cash in the air. "No, they didn't tell me why. There just ain't one, and there ain't nothing I can do about it!" At first the mob doesn't believe him, especially since there's one of McClellan's monstrous iron-and-copper contraptions just sitting there, apparently ready to go. "I can only do what they tell me to do," the clerk assures everyone, "and there just ain't going to be a stage today, and probably not tomorrow neither, from what I'm told." The folks are disappointed but quiet down eventually and disperse.

"Look at that," the inventor says as he strides up, some overburdened porters in tow. "A hundred dollars or so I'll never get back!" Professor McClellan strides in, shares a few words with his clerk, and motions the porters to drop their bundles in under the awning. "Brought a few things you folks could use, I reckon."

The Electric Stage

McClellan's invention is a large, enclosed coach with no hitch or buckboard. It's made mostly of wooden planks braced together everywhere with iron bands.

The wide wheels are entirely made of steel with thick copper wire wrapped all around the outside. Four thin pieces of copper protrude from under the carriage and slightly bend against the spokes of each wheel. The coach's insides are plush, and there's enough room for eight passengers.

The Professor grabs an oil can and squirts a bit here and there on the machine, wiping away dust where he sees it. "Got two of them," he says. "The other's at the end of the line and comes back here when this one leaves. They don't hit each other because they home in on that antenna." He points over to a steel tower that looks like a windmill without the blades. "You can take this one if you want to."

The Lighting Gun

The Professor's porters have brought a bunch of good rations and equipment: bullets and knives, hard tack and salted port, even some cigars and whiskey. The supplies are all bundled in large, canvas bags. One porter lugs a huge, black trunk that's way too heavy for him, and he lets it slam loudly onto the plank floor.

Professor McClellan's Lighting Gun

Shots	Speed	ROF	Damage	Range Inc	Price	Reliability
N/A	2	1/2	4d10	5	N/A	15

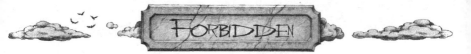

"Careful with that, you dag'berned fool!" The Professor leaps over to the trunk and examines it closely while giving the porter a wicked stare. "This thing's kind of fragile, you know! Come over here and look at this, folks."

"This has still got a patent pending on it back in Washington, but I guess it's okay if you use it out there in the Salt Flats where nobody can see ya usin' it. Who knows what sort of nasty critters you're going to run across while you're out there. It's a gun, like a Winchester, but instead of bullets it shoots out a bolt of lightning.

"It's McClellan's Sure-Fry Lightning Gun. I'm hoping to sell it to the army one day. I'm sure they could put it to use!"

The Professor turns the latch and opens the trunk to reveal a huge mass of copper tubes and gears. It's vaguely gun-shaped, but it's huge.

"The salt flats run the electric stage, and they can power the Lightning Gun too. All you have to do is drive these spikes into the ground out there, and the gun is all charged up and ready to go! Ought to be able to shoot it all day out there. No worries about reloading! You'll see when you fire it up!"

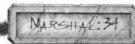

Fire in the Sky

Before the Lightning Gun can be fired, each steel spike has to be driven deep into the ground with a sledge hammer, which takes a hero 3 actions or two heroes 2 actions per spike. Once the spikes are in place, the gun can fire any number of times. The cables are only long enough to move the gun 10 feet from the spikes.

The gun draws electricity through the spikes, which makes the gun crackle. Gears turn, and a low-pitched whine gets higher and higher until it's charged. The process takes at least 5 full seconds, so the gun can only be fired every other round, between recharges.

The powerful bolt of electricity resembles a jagged lightning bolt. If the target is missed, the bolt dives harmlessly into the ground just beyond the target.

Malfunction

Minor: The gun fizzles and sputters. A Fair (5) *Cognition* roll reveals that one of the spikes is loose, and not making good connection with the ground.

Major: The gun shorts out and blows the cables off the housing. A Hard (9) *tinkerin'* roll is required to fix it.

Catastrophe: The gun arcs and explodes, doing 3d10 damage to everyone within 10 yards.

Saddle Up

Professor McClellan's feelings aren't hurt at all if the heroes decide not to take his electric stage out onto the flats. "I'm not sure I'd want to ride along where some folks had their hearts ripped out either."

The stage itself is not important to the rest of the adventure. The heroes can use it or go by horse or foot.

It's a hot, dry day when the adventurers take off. Even the gentle winds kick up quite a bit of the salty dust, stinging the eyes and clogging the throat, making white clouds that are hard to see through.

It's not like a true sandstorm, but it's difficult going, even with a kerchief tied tight around the face. Before the heroes have gone a mile, Salt Lake City's sprawl is completely obscured by the swirling grit.

Stage Trip

McClellan's Electric Stage is darned comfortable, that's for sure. The seats are plush and soft, and there are several layers of springs between the passengers' kiesters and the rough ground. It's a good, smooth ride, like a carriage rolling on one of them paved streets in Kansas City. Apparently McClellan takes his clientele's comfort seriously.

Of course, there are a couple of drawbacks too. When the thing gets rolling, there are quite a few zaps and sparks. The sensation is quite tingly at first, and before the heroes know it their hair's standing way up off their heads. When they touch someone, they get a big zap. The stage is speedy, about twice as fast as a horse-drawn stage at a trot, and the stage's motor never tires.

The stage has windows that can be raised and lowered, but they're up now to keep the blowing dust outside. Through the front glass, the heroes can see the well-traveled trail that this thing has taken before, just two ruts in an otherwise unbroken sea of salt and dust.

By Foot or Horse

The electric stage looks harmless enough, but some folks just died in it recently, so why take a chance? Ackensack isn't that far across the salt flats. People have crossed them before, plenty of times, so it isn't like it's impossible.

The horses don't like the blowing salt because it stings their eyes real bad, so the heroes need to cover their mounts' heads and walk them. The trail's easy enough to follow, though, without even having to look up into the swirling grit. Still, the bright sun off the white salt gives the heroes headaches before long.

Time and Distance

There's nothing on the salt flats more interesting than some far-off rattlers and dust storms, until the heroes reach the exact center and find the wrecked galleon.

By electric stage, the trip takes just into the evening. By horse or foot, the heroes reach the ship in the dark hours of the early morning—if they decide to travel through the night.

Chapter Two: Ghost Ship

The heroes can't see the smashed galleon as they approach. The electric stage simply loses power and rolls to a stop about 100 feet short of the galleon. The loss of locomotion is a mystery.

There is nothing obviously wrong, and any of the posse members that investigate the stage are unable to solve the problem. If they came on foot any horses get restless at that distance and refuse to advance.

There's plenty of debris around the wreck, especially to its port (west) side. Both the anchor and rudder lay half buried in the salty ground, 20 yards off the port side, in an area littered with splintered boards. The characters may come across a piece of this debris (a copper pitcher, olive jar, or an ancient Spanish coin) or even an item of a more seafaring nature (like the anchor or a bit of the net rigging) before they actually set eyes on the smashed ship itself.

The approaching heroes don't get a good look at the galleon until they're right on top of it, either because they are approaching in the dark or because blowing, salty dust obscures it in the daylight. Let the heroes approach the ship cautiously, but there's nothing obviously dangerous when they find the galleon.

Nobody Here But Us Chickens

Everything's damned quiet out here, except for the howling winds, and there's nothing particular to see, but it sure feels queer. Then all of a sudden there's creaking, like an old barn heaving against the wind and a fluttering like tattered flags.

Just when the heroes are trying to figure out what that is, the dust clears, and there's this huge thing laying there on the ground. It's all smashed wood and beams with long poles and ropes catching the wind here and there.

It's huge and creepy. Any hero that makes an Onerous (7) *Knowledge* roll can tell it's an old Spanish galleon.

Narvaez in the Desert

The galleon is a large vessel, just over 100 feet long. When seaworthy, it could carry 400 tons of cargo, and it mounted five cannons to either side. The *Narvaez* was typical of the galleon style of its day, with a heavy beakhead and a pronounced forecastle (both toward the bow) and a towering sterncastle and gallery (both to the aft). These ships plied the Caribbean in the heyday of the conquistadors, carrying gold and other plunder to Spain.

The present-day *Narvaez*, however, suffered great damage from the hurricane that struck her, the impact as it landed here in the salt flats, and 300 years of neglect.

Initial Investigation

The heroes are free to circle the outside of the ship. The port side of the lower hull has been smashed, crushing floor timbers and splintering the inner and outer planking, so now the vessel lists 20° in that direction. The deck planking has fallen through, and most of the forecastle is just missing. Of the three masts, only two are still erect, while the aft mast has fallen forward through the rigging and leans off the starboard side of the ship, the tip of it embedded deep in the salty ground. Tattered bits of sail still cling to the masts by frayed ropes.

All the soft materials—the wood, ropes, and sails—are extremely worn and useless. The wood still holds together, but in places it crumbles easily at a touch. The ropes cannot hold much weight, certainly not the weight of a hero. If any of the heroes try climbing them, the ropes break under the stress. The iron fittings and lead lower-hull plating are still strong, but most of it is rusted or bent. If the heroes are reluctant to enter the wreck, entice them with a handful of gold coins lying on the ground.

Into the Hulk

A close examination of the outside of the ship shows three cracks in the hull through which a hero could enter: under the wreck of the forecastle on the starboard side, along the aft port side opposite the third mast, and along the aft where the rudder assembly was broken away by the impact. If the heroes venture on top of the ship, they find another entrance through the now-rotted leather grating over the main cargo hold. The smashed beams and timbers make all four of these possible entrances narrow and dangerous.

The heroes may elect to cut through some other portion of the ship with axes. The wood is quite fragile an easy to cut, though the lead sheeting over the hull is difficult to pry away. Such a project is possible, though difficult, taking four hours of bending and chopping, or six hours if they're using inferior equipment.

In the Event of Fire...

The wreck of the *Narvaez* is highly flammable. The wood has been drying for 300 years, and it ignites with the slightest spark. It may occur to the adventurers to set the galleon ablaze to kill whatever's inside.

Whenever the main wreck is set on fire, it takes only one minute for the fire to really get going, and just 10 minutes until the entire ship is engulfed. At that time, all the remaining undead in the ship (we'll get to them in a moment) emerge at once to attack the adventurers; the undead below ground remain undisturbed and must be rooted out later. The ship burns down to cooling coals in 5 hours.

Let the adventurers know the wreck is ready to burn. Any torches or sparks set a nearby beam burning, and though it's easily put out, this should send a powerful message of fire safety to the posse.

Light

Torches are out of the question, though covered lanterns can be brought in. Otherwise, the wreck is splintered enough that a small amount of daylight filters through. Shafts of light get into every section, at least enough so that adventurers can see what they're doing if they go in during the day. A gust of wind can blow up enough dust to block that for a minute or two, which may be a good way to build suspense.

Fear

The Fear Level around the galleon is 3.

Gold and Silver Treasure

There are 170 Spanish coins scattered around the ship in various places. Twenty lay around outside within 50 yards of the wreck, and another 20 are each in the five main areas (the collapsed sterncastle and gallery, the partially collapsed rear hold, the open main hold, the smashed forward hold, and the open bow compartments), and then 50 gold coins and 275 silver coins are in the rotting chest located in de Velasco's underground chamber. The underground chambers run beneath the ship, and they are described in detail in Chapter Three.

Finding all the scattered coins takes a Hard (9) *search* roll in each area. Gold coins are worth $20. Silver coins are worth $5.

Collapsed Sterncastle and Gallery

The timbers are split and broken sharp all around where the rudder has been broken away, so it's hard to get inside without cutting yourself or snagging your clothes. Inside, three layers of the ship have collapsed down, crushing the different floors together so there's nowhere to stand up. If the heroes are going in through the aft of the ship, they're going to have to crawl.

Officers lived and worked in this part of the ship, and their belongings are all scattered around. There are copper bowls and utensils here and there, and a couple of trunks of rotten clothes dumped out. There are also some personal possessions, like a broken hand mirror, combs and brushes. With a Fair (5) *search* roll, the heroes find a large, leather-bound book, the diary of Captain Diego de Velasco, a Spanish adventurer who was on the *Narvaez* three centuries ago. See the props at the back of the book for the most vital excerpts.

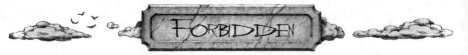

Getting through this collapsed portion of the galleon is difficult. In a half an hour or so, the heroes can get through to the partially collapsed rear hold or even out onto the top "deck" of the ship, though the latter is badly damaged and difficult to walk on.

Of course, the entire place is crawling with large, black, undead wharf rats. There are 30 of them here, ready to fight. The rats attack when the posse is in confined spaces, so they can easily bite on the head and face, shoulders and back, and anywhere else that's exposed.

Undead Wharf Rats

The wharf rats draw their energy directly from the idol of the Forbidden God. The rats seek out living things, but since there are usually none out on the salt flats, they consume bits of each other. They're half rotted away, baring their bones, and their eyes shine with an evil glare.

Profile

Corporeal: D:1d4, N:1d4, S:1d4, Q:1d10+2, V:1d4
Fighting: Brawling 4d6
Mental: C:1d6, K:1d4, M:1d4, Sm:1d4, Sp:1d4
Size: 1
Terror: 5
Special Abilities:
Bite: STR
Rot: If an undead wharf rat causes a wound, its spittle infects the injury with a rotting disease. The victim must make a Hard (9) *Vigor* roll immediately. If successful, the rotting disease doesn't take hold. If the roll is failed, the flesh starts rotting away at the rate of one wound level per full day. When the body part becomes maimed, it has rotted off entirely. Before this point, the decay can be halted entirely with a Hard (9) *medicine* roll. Harrowed are immune to the rotting disease.
Undead.

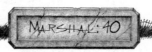

Partially Collapsed Rear of Hold

The aft third of the cargo hold is only partially crushed. The deck above this area, which includes the forward parts of the sterncastle, is still pretty much in place. Some of the planking has buckled and bowed toward the starboard side, leaving just enough headroom for a man to walk without having to stoop for fear of knocking his head.

The main obstacles are the large hull planks that have splintered upward from the impact with the ground, making a forest of jagged, broken beams. This portion of the hold is cut off from the rest of the cargo hold by a thick wall of these upward-thrust beams. To get through them in either direction, the heroes have to remove them, which should take a fair amount of time.

Any of the heroes that make an Onerous (7) *search* roll find an opening through the splintered hull planking. If the hero investigates the opening, she finds a narrow tunnel dug into the salt flats below. This is the entrance to the underground chambers where the undead crew of the ship are now located, which are described on page 55.

The rear of the hold held the ship's supplies and provisions. There are barrels and crates smashed everywhere, some filled with hazelnuts, hickory acorns, coconuts, and fruit, but all of it is now dried and useless.

There is still a faint aroma of rotten food in the stale air. There are piles of bones from pigs, cows, sheep, and goats that were slaughtered to feed the crew. But wherever folks store food, there are going to be roaches, and the ones on the *Narvaez* are hungry!

Undead Roaches

These are not run-of-the-mill roaches! There are about 100 here. Every round, each nearby hero has 1d3 body parts (roll on the Hit Location Table to choose which ones) swarmed by 1d4 roaches. They can all be brushed off a body part by winning a *Strength* contest. On any hit against them, roll 1d6. On 1–2, it hits the roach's head. Otherwise, it hits the gizzards.

Profile

Corporeal: D:1d4, N:1d4, S:1d4, Q:1d6, V:1d4
Mental: C:1d4, K:1d4, M:1d4, Sm:1d4, Sp:1d4
Size: 1
Terror: 5
Special Abilities:
Bite: STR
Undead.

Main Hold

The port side of the main hold is splintered outward onto the salt flats like some huge, bucktoothed grin. The starboard side of the hold, though, is relatively open, with a clear space about 10 yards wide and 20 yards long.

The hold (or what's left of it) is stacked with crates filled with broken pottery. More broken pottery is scattered all over the ship's floor. There are also piles of cow hides, probably a couple of hundred of them, but they're all dry and brittle now, so they crumble when picked up.

All along the walls are hooks and chains where slaves were held on the ship. In one spot, the hull planking has been completely broken away to reveal the salty earth beneath the ship.

If the heroes poke around in here too long, though, there's a shaggy beast waiting in the shadows to kill them.

Zombie Steer

This lone abomination is mostly just bones, with its loose skin draped over a few remaining muscles and organs. But its jagged and splintered horns are dangerous, and it can charge between the crates.

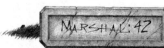

Profile

Corporeal: D:1d8, N:2d8, S:2d12, Q:3d8, V:2d10+2 Fighting Brawling 4d8
Mental: C:2d6, K:1d4, M:2d4, Sm:1d4, Sp:2d6
Size: 8
Terror: 7
Special Abilities:
Gore: STR+2d6
Undead.

Smashed Forward Hold

The thick supports that used to span the height of the forward hold are now squashed and split like a bunch of broken fingers, and the splinters are sharp as porcupine quills. There is enough head room for the heroes to walk around without knocking their heads. There isn't much junk thrown around in here, so it was probably empty when the ship was dumped here in the salt flats. Above, the netting is hanging loose in places in the main opening to the old deck. The hold is full of the bones of dead horses and cattle.

The heroes can see the signs of a recent disturbance in the dust: footprints and places where bodies have fallen and been dragged off toward the open hold area. A Fair (5) *trackin'* roll reveals four combatants and at least two victims.

A few minutes of searching the forward hold reveals a lady's locket with a broken chain, a smashed derby with a "Salt Lake's Haberdashers" label, and a ticket stub from Professor McClellan's Electric Stage. The professor's last customers went through here, and they certainly didn't go peacefully.

There's something else, though, deeper through the dust. Posse members who make an Onerous (7) *search* roll discover a strange image burnt into the hold's floor.

It's six feet across, with intricate images of all kinds around a circular pattern. Most are indistinguishable, but there is definitely a sailing ship with an enormous wave about to crush it. There's also a demon's face in the hold of the ship. The rest is indecipherable. This image was integral to Pohqui's hex that brought on the hurricane that wrecked the *Narvaez*, which a hero might realize on a Hard (9) *academia: occult* roll.

Open Bow Compartments

The *Narvaez*'s sailors lived in short bunks stacked tightly into the bow compartments in the front of the hold. These poor Spaniards were only modestly paid and tended not to share in the ship's bounty.

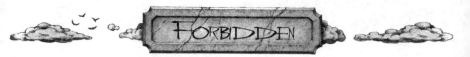

Most of them were pressed into service. Now the bunks of the unfortunate swabs remain surprisingly intact, but slightly canted to port.

The single portal from the hold to the crew bunks cannot be seen until a light is brought right up to it. The heroes may be startled (Fair (3) *guts* checks) to see the wood of the bunkroom carved with hundreds of crosses, some as small as a thumb, others a foot high. Tarnished silver crosses on chains hang from pegs, alongside dusty rosaries. This was obviously an attempt at protection or comfort from some form of evil.

Broken boards and planks were once nailed across the entrance. The whole area is blackened and scorched from a long, desperate struggle to keep something deemed unholy at bay.

Before the hurricane 300 years ago, the sailors on the *Narvaez* knew that an accursed presence had invaded their ship. When they knew their captain, de Velasco, had succumbed to its power, they barricaded themselves in their quarters. Their final struggle went for naught, and their bones are scattered everywhere around the hold, their chests split wide open.

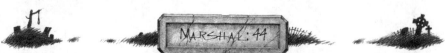

Heroes making a Fair (5) *Cognition* roll note the remnants of the sailors' makeshift weapons. Perfectly good harpoons, now corroded, have a small board lashed perpendicularly onto the handle. Clubs are similarly adorned, and even the various cutlasses lying about. The sailors had turned all their weapons into thrusting weapons in the shape of a cross. None of their weapons are in usable condition now, however.

Another successful Fair (5) *Cognition* roll alerts the characters to a simple carving inside one of the old bunks. This one shows the ship, smashed and listing as it is now, with an "X" marking the location of the entrance to the underground passages that has been created underneath the ship.

If one of the heroes makes a Hard (9) *search* roll, she finds a crude carving of an early map of the underground chambers, located on the underside of a bunk. The map is tagged with a line in Spanish that hints at the treasure of the "savage Captain." If the heroes find the map then finding de Velasco's treasure in the underground chambers should be easier.

The handful of silver crosses in the crew quarters are worth $25.

Diary of a Madman

In the collapsed sterncastle, the characters may have found the leather-bound journal of Diego de Velasco, a Spanish adventurer who lived more than 300 years ago. If the heroes did not find it, place it elsewhere in the *Narvaez* for them to discover.

Using the Journal

The information in the journal of Captain De Velasco (see page 62) is important for the adventurers to understand what they're dealing with. The captain kept a complete log of the events aboard the *Narvaez*, and his fall into darkness is recorded in the journal.

The journal is extremely old and fragile. It is written in Spanish. If the ship is burned to the ground before the characters find the journal, remove it to some other location early in their underground explorations. (See Chapter Four.)

Bounty

The posse defeats the wharf rats or the roaches: 1 white chip for each.
The posse defeats the zombie steer: 1 red chip.
The posse finds the maps: 1 white chip.
The posse finds the underground entrance: 1 white chip.

Chapter Three: Evil Presences

When the heroes enter the underground chambers they risk possession by the spirits of Captain de Velasco or Pohqui the medicine woman. Only face cards indicate possession, and the first hero that draws a face card of each color is affected. Have the heroes draw cards at random, and apply the results listed in the possession sections on the following pages. Each spirit may attempt to possess a hero each time the posse enters a new area. Each spirit may only possess one hero at a time.

The Grinning Spaniard, Diego de Velasco

In his day, Diego de Velasco was a gentleman of the Spanish court. Dashing, and considered quite handsome for his time, de Velasco knew many women of quality.

He was a skilled rider and swordsman, and he was especially well-trained with the rapier. De Velasco won several duels in Spain and slew many "savages" in Yucatan with his blade.

He dreamed of making his fortune in the New World and retiring to a large estate in his native Castile. His ambitions eventually led to his demise, and he is now trapped in his own nightmare.

De Velasco was once a notable man, but now he's an undead prisoner. Two foul curses and three centuries of unending war against the other undead have driven the former conquistador absolutely mad. He is completely evil, and he abhors everything about the living. He will kill any intruders in order to offer their heart to the Forbidden God.

De Velasco is a shambling corpse with drawn, blackened skin. His eyes are gone, leaving only black sockets beneath the brim of his rusted helmet, and his yellowed teeth show through a permanent grin stretched open by his receding facial skin.

In addition to his helm, he's armored with a breastplate, and wears tattered remnants of a silk shirt and pantaloons. De Velasco still wields his deadly rapier with a special skill for removing the hearts of his unfortunate opponents.

De Velasco was driven completely insane by the magical powers of the Aztec god's bowl. In a matter of just a few weeks, he went from a greedy but pious Spanish adventurer to a bloodthirsty killer. He terrorized the colonists, slaves, and finally the crew on the galleon, chasing down victims and cutting out their hearts for his precious golden bowl.

When de Velasco possesses a character, it insists on using Spanish if called upon to speak. This may alert savvy heroes to their friend's plight.

Profile

Corporeal: D:1d10, N:3d10, S:2d12+2, Q:2d10, V:4d12
Fightin': rapier 6d10, sneak 2d8
Mental: C:3d8, K:1d4, M:3d8, Sm:1d12, Sp:4d8
Search 3d10, tracking 6d10
Size: 8
Terror: 11
Special Abilities:
Undead.
Heart Rip: When striking with his rapier, De Velasco always hits to the gizzards.
Possession: See below.

Possession by De Velasco

Incomplete Takeover (J♣ or Q♣, J♠ or Q♠): De Velasco's spirit fails to completely control the hero's mind, but the grip it takes leaves permanent scars on the unfortunate victim. The character's mind is awash with images of jungles, sailing ships, columns of chained slaves.

The most horrific images, though, are of the countless, bloody murders. The hero can't ever forget the images she witnesses from this attempted takeover, and it may affect her in the future. She lapses into fluent Spanish easily for the next few minutes, even if she's never spoken the language before.

Overpower (K♣): The conquistador's spirit focuses a wild surge of magical energy from the Hunting Grounds into the character. Ghostly images of horrible murder and torture flood the area for every member of the posse to see.

De Velasco's spirit doesn't take control of the hero, but the hero is well aware that another presence nearly took control of his mind.

Extroverted Bloodlust (K♠): De Velasco's manitou takes control of the hero, but its rage doesn't allow it to masquerade as a mere mortal. The manitou is out for blood, and nothing can stop it.

He rants wildly in Spanish about his fortune and serving the forbidden god Coutzlatl, then immediately looks for a sacrificial victim and lashes out at his companions with all his weapons, hoping to drag one down and rip out her heart with a knife.

If successful, the hero-turned-killer races for the partially collapsed rear hold, fresh heart in hand, and then down to the golden bowl in the south chamber of the underground. This takes about one minute. Every 30 seconds (six combat rounds), the hero can try to win a *Spirit* contest to regain control.

Once there, the spirit directs the hero to draw his knife and plunge it into his own chest. At that moment, the hero can try to win another *Spirit* contest to regain control. If he does not, the knife plunges through his heart, and the hero's body collapses, gushing blood from a ghastly wound and into the golden bowl.

Introverted Bloodlust (A♣): The de Velasco spirit takes control of the hero's body, but it has the presence of mind to realize that it already has a heart for its bloodthirsty Aztec god: the hero's. He calmly and quietly walks toward the partially collapsed rear hold and then down into the underground and the south chamber. This takes about three minutes.

The manitou is trying to maintain a low profile. The spirit has the adventurer walk at first, but he breaks into a run if his companions try to stop him. See above for details.

Call to Arms (A♠): The conquistador takes over the hero's body long enough to scream in a foul tongue. The shrill voice is not the hero's, and seconds later when the spirit releases him, he doesn't remember having screamed it. The call awakens and releases the undead Spanish sailors in the underground, who now stalk the adventurers in search of their hearts.

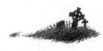

Tlaxcalan Witch, Pohqui the Medicine Woman

Pohqui was a rural medicine woman of the Tlaxcalan people. Since she lived a relatively simple life, objects of pleasure, such as books, toys, and games (including decks of cards) also draw her anger. She tears these to bits after slaying their owners.

In life she traveled from village to village, delivering healing medicines and casting helpful hexes. When enslaved on the Spanish galleon *Narvaez,* she sensed the presence of the golden bowl and knew how it would affect its owner, Diego de Velasco. It was Pohqui's magic that called the great hurricane to deliver the doomed galleon to the lifeless salt flats, where she hoped the idol would wither and die without living hearts to feed upon.

Pohqui lived for over 100 years after her capture by de Velasco, but her body finally succumbed to the test of time, and she became one of the undead inhabiting the lower chambers. Although she despises her current state of unlife, she clings to this world, determined to make sure that the evil that's possessed de Velasco is forever prevented from returning to the lands of the living.

The witch is covered with the powdery salt. It has collected over the years into the deep wrinkles of her brown skin, where it has crusted and turned virtually solid. When she moves, the caked salt falls away from her body in a fine, white powdery cloud.

Her mouth is stuffed full with salt and her eyes are nothing more than jagged, white crystals. She is loathe to attack the living unless she determines that it's the only way to stop the savage captain of the *Narvaez.*

Whereas de Velasco's violence is completely undirected, Pohqui has a keen sense of right and wrong. Her spirit wishes only to maintain the status quo, keeping the idol here in the salt flats. Pohqui has been able to control her manitou most of the time, but occasionally the manitou takes over, much to Pohqui's remorse.

Profile

Corporeal: D:3d8, N:5d12, S:3d8, Q:3d10, V:2d6

Dodge 8d12, fightin': brawlin' 5d12, sneak 4d12

Mental: C:2d8, K:1d4, M:2d8, Sm:2d6, Sp:4d8

Terror: 11

Special Abilities:

Undead.

Possession: See the next page.

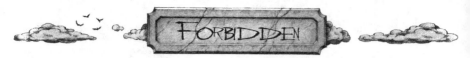

Possession by Pohqui

Incomplete Takeover (J♦ or Q♦, J♥ or Q♥): The hero lapses for several (1d6) minutes into an ancient language that no one understands. During that time, the adventurer stammers, wavering and finally falling to the ground as his mind races through an exotic series of the medicine woman's memories. He sees the tall, brightly painted temples in populous jungle cities, someone grinding herbs and roots with a mortar and pestle, and Spanish "devils" wielding whips in their bright armor. The images are very real and leave the hero shaken for several minutes after they subside.

Fear (K♦): Pohqui's spirit reasons that the best way to drive the living away from the golden bowl is to frighten them. It unleashes a couple of minutes of horrible images into the mind of the controlled hero: ancient blood rituals and mutilations performed on himself and his companions. Likewise, it casts a special *fear* power through the adventurer on his companions, forcing them to lose -1 step of *Coordination* and *Speed* for the next hour of game time, and all *guts* checks should be made at -4. Heroes may resist the effects of this spell with a Hard (9) *Spirit* roll.

Reason (K♥): The medicine woman's spirit figures it can reason with the heroes to get them to clear out and keep others from coming out this way. It speaks through the possessed hero, in English, telling them of the cursed golden bowl and its thirst for fresh hearts. The hero, entranced by the controlling spirit, explains how it only seeks hearts when it senses them, and out here in the salt flats it's pretty much harmless. The spirit doesn't respond to questions, but after it has gone, the hero feels he was controlled by a benevolent, truthful presence.

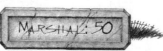

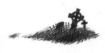

Sacrifice (A♦): Pohqui's spirit decides it is willing to sacrifice itself, and the hero it now controls, for a chance to destroy the golden bowl of Coutzlatl. The hero screams in the ancient Tlaxcalan language and races away from his fellows toward the south chamber of the underground. This takes about 30 seconds. On the way, the hero has one chance to win a *Spirit* contest to regain control. Once there, the hero gets one last attempt to win a *Spirit* contest.

If the hero fails, Pohqui's energy battles against Coutzlatl's in a brilliant display. This is a contested *Spirit* roll combining Pohqui's roll with the hero's (add his raises to her roll) against the idol's *Spirit* of 6d12.

If Pohqui wins, the bowl vanishes, and she leaves the hero's body. He's completely aware of her victory and her motivations against the evil in the bowl. If Coutzlatl's bowl wins, Pohqui's soul is destroyed, along with that of the unfortunate hero.

Wanton Destruction (A♥): The medicine woman's spirit elects to slay all living heroes to keep them from feeding Coutzlatl's bowl. The possessed hero attacks his fellow heroes until he's subdued. When it's over, the hero's face is wet with tears, and he feels tremendous remorse on Pohqui's part.

Chapter Four: The Salty Underground

The characters reach the underground when they discover the narrow tunnel dug into the ground under the partially collapsed rear-hold of the *Narvaez*. They may discover it while searching the ship, or they may come across it after the old galleon's hulk has burned to the ground. Either way, the underground area is unaffected and ready for exploration. The map for the underground lair is on page 61.

Chambers and Passages

The underground complex was dug by the undead that were left after the wreck of the *Narvaez*. The light of day irritates these undead, and the remains of the hulk served poorly to block it out.

The complex was excavated using tools improvised from what was left on the ship, or bones and fingernails. The walls, floors, and ceilings are uneven and crumbling with salty dirt. The ceilings and passages are supported with crumbling beams from the galleon wreck. Without these, the entire underground complex would fall in on itself.

The Entrance

The entrance to the underground chambers is located underneath the rear hold of the *Narvaez.* It is narrow, but the crumbling dirt makes it easy to slide down through the confined space to a small chamber.

After the heroes enter the underground, they may encounter 1d3 Tlaxcalan zombies or "heartless" undead soldiers in the passages. (See page 56–58.)

Draw a card. On red, the heroes find Tlaxcalans. On black, the heroes find soldiers. On a Joker, they find both, battling it out against each other. If the posse comes upon one of these battles, the undead immediately stop fighting among themselves and attack the heroes.

The Captain's Quarters

Captain de Velasco feels life (with the help of a certain medicine woman) cheated him out of his rightful position of power. He still feels he is the captain of the *Narvaez.* Many of his belongings from the ship have been moved to this room, and he has decorated this chamber in a fashion that resembles his cabin as it was on the ship.

His captain's desk and chair reside against the far wall, and the walls are lined with bookshelves full of ancient and crumbling books. An old navigational map is spread across his desk, and it appears the captain still plots courses to the new world. The captain is not in his quarters.

An image of the idol of the forbidden god is scratched in the wall behind his desk. Coutzlatl obviously occupies de Velasco's thoughts to this day.

The treasure of de Velasco is located down the passage that leads out of his chamber, and it is marked with an "X" on the map. If the heroes found the map in the bow compartments of the ship, they can find the treasure on an Fair (5) *search* roll. If they did not find the carving, it takes an Incredible (11) *search* roll to locate the chest.

The Heartless Soldiers' Quarters

The soldiers that are still controlled by de Velasco reside in these chambers. There are various weapons lying in and around the corners of the room. Most of the weapons are rusted and of no use.

De Velasco tries to maintain the chain of command over his men. The quarters, in some ways, still resemble those of a Spanish soldier.

There are rusted helmets and breastplates (all of which have the chests ripped out) on

makeshift shelves around the room. Other supplies that are normally found in a barracks are scattered around the area.

At any given time, there are one or two undead soldiers in the room. They immediately attack any intruders with their ancient rapiers.

The Lair of the Forbidden God

This chamber holds the idol of the forbidden god. The idol, gleaming in the light of the lanterns, can be seen squatting in the chamber.

The golden bowl of Coutzlatl rests in the northwest corner of the chamber, still hungry for the beating hearts of living sacrifices. The magic of the bowl has some control over the undead, sending them to fight against the living to feed its thirst for blood. The bowl's magic can manifest itself into a powerful apparition of Coutzlatl himself, but the forbidden god prefers to do its work through its undead subjects.

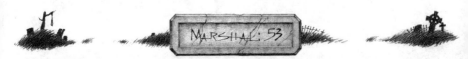

When the heroes enter this room, they are immediately confronted by de Velasco and two of his undead soldiers. If the heroes have not encountered Pohqui (or if she was unable to possess one of the characters), she appears in the chamber two rounds after the final confrontation begins, and she attacks Captain de Velasco.

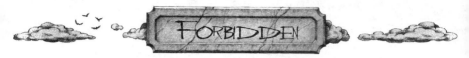

Pohqui's Chamber of Black Magic

This is the lair of Pohqui. The room is filled with relics of black magic and items used for enchantments. Her spirit is hovering in the chamber, and she openly communicates with the heroes.

She tries to convince the heroes that their only solution to ending this bloody curse of the forbidden god is to kill Captain de Velasco. He will continue to sacrifice victims as they cross the salt flats, unless he is vanquished. She tells them that the captain is located in the chamber containing the idol, and she assists them if possible.

If the posse does not agree to go after de Velasco, she once again attempts to possess a hero (choose one randomly) to go after the captain. If she fails to possess one of the characters, her spirit flees the room, screeching violently.

Zombie Lair

There are several chambers in the complex where Tlaxcalan zombies live. There

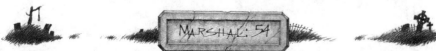

are one or two zombies in the room at any given time. The zombies attack any of the heroes on sight, unless the posse has encountered Pohqui and agreed to her terms. If the posse is not willing to help Pohqui, the zombies attack.

Treasure

There are 13 gold ingots scattered around on the ground (marked with a "G" on the map). An Onerous (7) *search* roll is required to find each. Every bar is worth $75.

Other Dangers

Dust

If the heroes shoot guns, it's going to kick up some dust. A thick layer of dust is settled on everything in the underground, and the passage of adventurers and zombies stirs up quite a bit of it. Usually it's just an annoyance–forcing the living to cover their faces with bandannas–until there's a gunfight.

Once bullets start to fly, loads of dust fall from the rafters and lift off the floor, obscuring vision and stinging the character's eyes. This can really cause problems in a fight.

Each round after gunfire begins–until three rounds after the shooting stops–characters must make a Fair (5) *Vigor* task to avoid rubbing their eyes and choking, rendering them useless for the round.

Complex Collapse

This underground complex isn't terribly stable (zombies aren't created for construction). Every chamber has bracing beams, and every passage has planking to hold the walls up.

Normal gunfire doesn't bring the ceiling down, but a raucous brawl might. Any time someone goes bust on a *Nimbleness*, *Deftness*, or *Strength*-based roll, the character must make an Onerous (7) *Nimbleness* task to keep from bumping a vital support column.

Failure means the ceiling collapses, which takes two combat rounds. In the first, enough dirt falls to let everyone know the whole thing's coming down. Anyone still hanging around in the second round has to make an Onerous (7) *Quickness* roll to do so. Failure means the hero gets buried underneath a pile of salty dirt and rubble.

Digging someone out is not too difficult if the rescuers are unopposed. (Of course, this assumes there are rescuers to begin with.) The dirt is fairly loose, and the victim can hold his breath for a minute or more. But if the adventurers are engaged in a fight, that's a different story.

Light and Fire

It's darker than pitch down here, and if you put a torch to it, the wood is going to burn. The rafters are just as dried and susceptible to fire as the rest of the shipwreck on the surface of the flats, but there aren't very many of them.

A flame put to any of them ignites all the beams in a chamber or passage, filling the entire complex with smoke and collapsing the area in four rounds. This works as described above, but the heroes have two rounds to move freely and two rounds in which they have to makes Onerous (7) *Quickness* rolls to move.

The Creatures

The underground is home to two warring factions of undead. The first is the hulking carcass of de Velasco himself, with his Spaniard minions. The other is the medicine woman Pohqui and her zombie followers.

Neither side has any way to utterly destroy the other, so the war has devolved into infrequent skirmishes over the last few decades. Both sides share the undead hatred of living beings and attack intruding heroes upon sight. Only Pohqui still fights against the forbidden god's desires.

The Heartless Spanards

The terrified crew and soldiers that remained alive when the hurricane swept the their galleon out of the Caribbean may have survived the storm, but their only reward for living through one terror was to endure another. They became de Velasco's next victims in his quest for human hearts and the blood of sacrificial victims.

Even with their hearts taken from them, the powerful magic of their deaths kept them from passing on to the next world. They now wander the chambers under the *Narvaez* as undead soldiers, still under the conquistador's control.

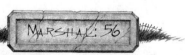

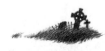

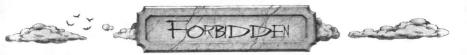

The heartless Spaniards are horrid ghouls with bluish-green, dripping skin and narrow, yellow eyes. Their chests are still open wide, showing where their hearts were removed so many years ago (by their own captain, no less) just to appease the forbidden god Coutzlatl. They still serve their captain, but not of their own will

Their clothes are nothing but rags hanging in strips from their bony carcasses, and though some of the former soldiers still have bits of armor or helmets, these are so corroded that they are useless in combat.

The soldiers instantly attack any living foes they find.

Profile

Corporeal: D:2d6, N:2d8, S:3d8, Q:2d10, V:2d8

Fightin': rapier 3d8, dodge 2d8

Mental: C:2d10, K:1d6, M:1d6, Sm:1d6, Sp:1d4

Overawe 5d6

Size: 6

Terror: 9

Gear: Rusted breastplates (chest ripped out) and helmets (each provide Armor 1), rusted rapiers (Reliability of 16; the sword breaks if the roll is failed).

Special Abilities:

Undead.

Tlaxcalan Zombie

Many of the slaves that were carried aboard the *Narvaez* died as the ship smashed to the ground in the salt flats. These simple Indians were mostly chained in the hold during the storm and had no chance to survive. The tremendous magical forces at work, however, claimed them as undead. The zombies are dark skinned and dressed in rags.

Profile

Corporeal: D:2d6, N:2d8, S:3d8, Q:2d10, V:2d8
Fightin': brawlin' 3d8
Mental: C:2d10, K:1d6, M:1d6, Sm:1d6, Sp:1d4
Size: 6
Terror: 9
Special Abilities:
Undead.

The Cursed Idol of Coutzlatl

Adventurers who attempt to steal or destroy the golden sacrifice bowl set in motion an ancient hex. The bowl grows steadily warmer and warmer until it is too hot to touch and finally glows red-hot, igniting dried wood or clothing that it touches. No tools or schemes available to the heroes can be used to move the red-hot bowl. It is not meant to be removed from its location.

Concluding the Adventure

When the characters return to Salt Lake City to warn Professor McClellan, he's not a happy inventor. He is willing to believe the characters' story, saying, "I've seen plenty of weirder stuff, you know, so a sailing ship sitting in the middle of the desert sounds perfectly believable to me!

"It's a shame, though, that we couldn't get that idol. That would have helped to alleviate the losses we have suffered due to this unfortunate incident."

McClellan's not one to just accept that the evil bowl can't be moved. He scratches his chin as he looks off into the distance. Then he realizes that the heroes are staring at him.

"Oh, pardon me. I guess you are waiting for payment." McClellan hands the posse a money bag, and then gets up and excuses himself hurriedly from the party.

"Good luck, and thank you."

Bounty

For each zombie or heartless Spaniard defeated: 1 white chip.
The posse finds de Velasco's treasure: 1 red chip.
The posse helps Pohqui: 1 red chip.
The posse defeats Captain de Velasco: 1 blue chip.

The Heartless Spaniards (10)

Attack:
Rapier 3d8/2d8+1d4
Defense:
Dodge 2
Terror: 9
Special Abilities:
Undead.

Tlaxcalan Zombies (10)

Attack:
Punch 2d8/2d4
Claw 2d8/1d4
Bite 2d8/1d6
Defense:
Brawling 4
Terror: 9
Special Abilities:
Undead.

The Zombie Steer

Attack:
Stomp 2d8/2d8
Ram 2d8/1d12
Bite 2d8/2d6
Defense:
Dodge 2
Terror: 7
Special Abilities:
Gore: STR+1d6
Undead.

Undead Roaches (40)

Attack:
Bite 1d4/1d4
Defense:
Dodge 2
Terror: 5
Special Abilities:
Undead.

Undead Wharf Rats (20)

Attack:
Bite 1d4/1d4
Claw 1d4/1d4
Defense:
Dodge 2
Terror: 5
Special Abilities:
Rot.
Undead.

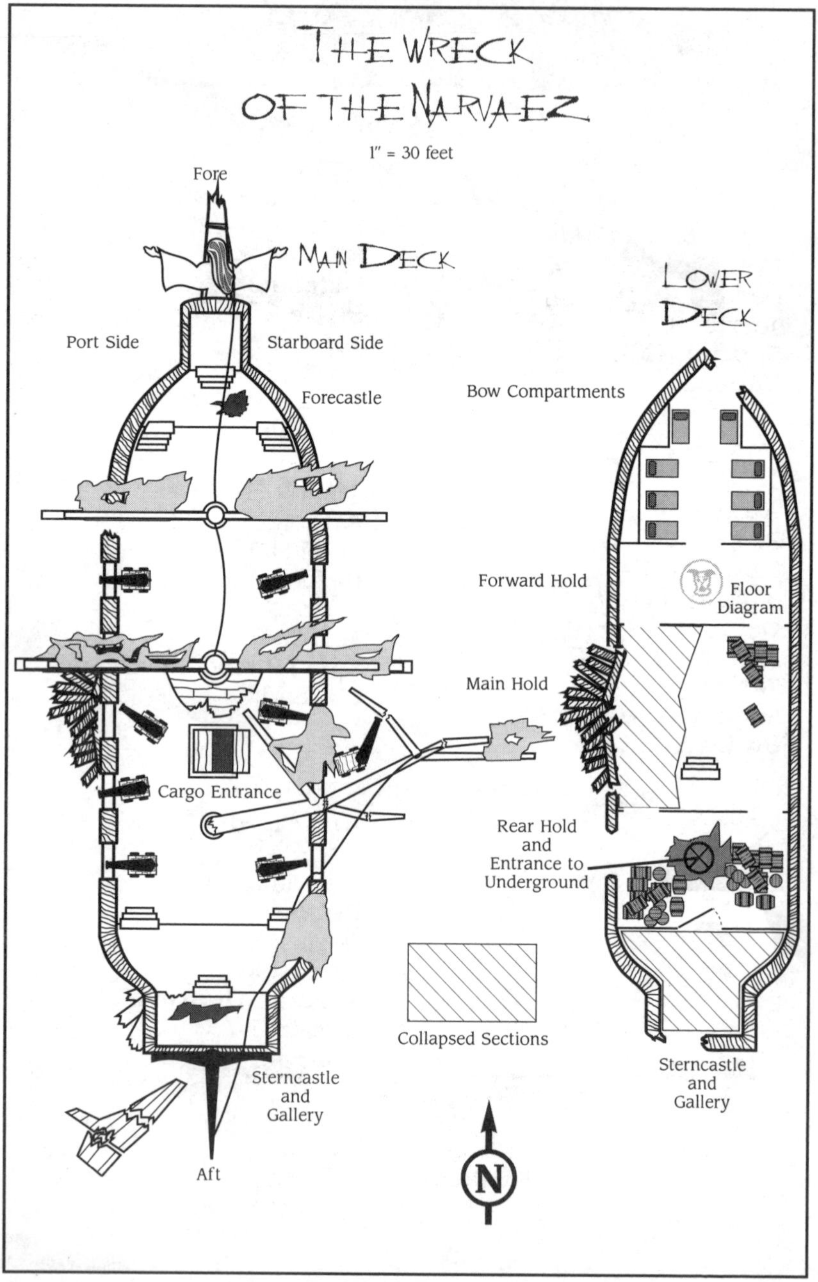
THE WRECK
OF THE NARVAEZ
1" = 30 feet
Fore
Main Deck
Lower Deck
Port Side
Starboard Side
Forecastle
Bow Compartments
Forward Hold
Floor
Diagram
Main Hold
Cargo Entrance
Rear Hold
and
Entrance to
Underground
Collapsed Sections
Sterncastle
and
Gallery
Sterncastle
and
Gallery
Aft
N

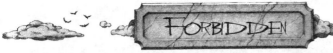

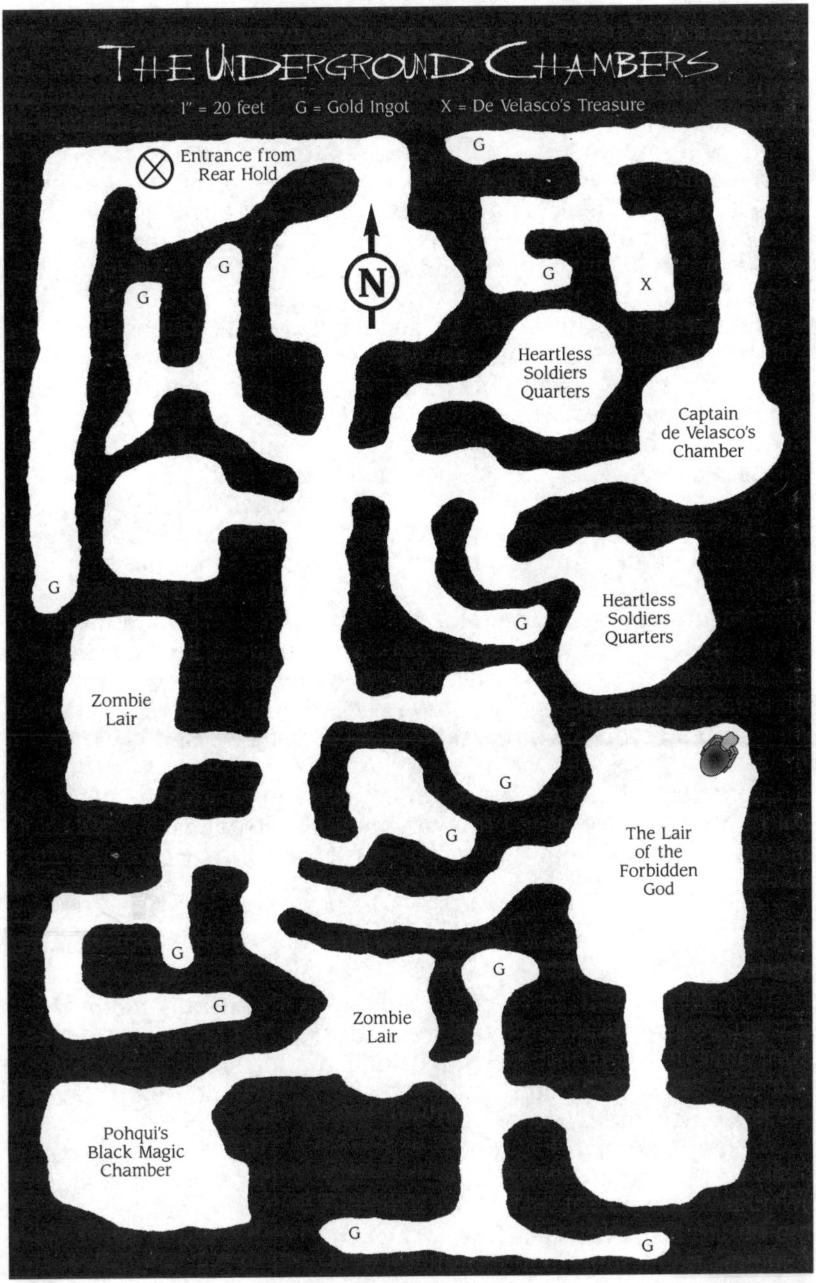
The Underground Chambers
1" = 20 feet
G = Gold Ingot
X = De Velasco's Treasure
Entrance from Rear Hold
N
G
G
G
G
X
Heartless Soldiers Quarters
Captain de Velasco's Chamber
G
G
Heartless Soldiers Quarters
Zombie Lair
G
G
The Lair of the Forbidden God
G
G
G
Zombie Lair
Pohqui's Black Magic Chamber
G
G

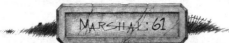

THE JOURNAL OF CAPTAIN DE VELASCO

April 15th, 1559, in the jungle wilderness of Veracruz, Mexico.

Earlier this evening, I awaited the appointed hour. I stood in the stinking jungle downpour, pulled my rain-soaked cloak tight around my chin with one hand while the other honored the Virgin with my Rosary. The jungle frightens me, and I am filled with fear for myself and my crew. This whole place is accursed by God! Blessed be the day I return to Castile! In the jungle, the silence was broken only by the steady rain, the hiss of cool droplets hitting my lantern, and my whispered prayers, until that man arrived.

The Aztec peasant appeared suddenly. He was just as I had met him earlier in the village, stoop shouldered from years of hard work in the maize fields, with a crazed and desperate look in his soulless eyes. The brown-skinned native carried his heavy burden over his shoulder, a wooden crate slung in a net. He eyed me cautiously until I pulled the small bag from beneath my cloak, emptied the gems into my palm for brief inspection, then replaced them and tossed it to the ground. The native dropped his crated burden into the undergrowth, grabbed up the bag of gems and ran off.

As I gathered the corners of the net and hoisted the crate over my shoulder I wondered: Were the Aztecs granted no wisdom by God? Why else would one trade a massive golden bowl for a handful of worthless gems? It was beyond my comprehension, but it must be divine intervention, and I feel that God is on my side.

Regardless of the reason, I am certainly fortunate the peasant made the trade. Now I have my own small fortune from the New World, and it will help me to obtain that which is rightfully mine.

July 12th, 1559, on board the galleon Narvaez in the Veracruz port of San Juan de Ulua

By order of the Viceroy we assemble the ships, 11 galleons and caravels, to depart within the week for Ochuse to the northeast. We will take colonists there to establish a fortress and new towns, including storehouses, homes, jails, inns, and even slaughterhouses.

Today I supervised loading barrels and crates filled with corn, hardtack, bacon, dried beef, cheese, oil, vinegar, and wine, along with live cattle and other animals. Tomorrow we load the arms and armor. When we leave we carry 540 soldiers, 240 horses, and more than 1,000 colonists and black servants, along with Aztec and Tlaxcalan slaves to work the fields.

The Journal of Captain De Velasco

But the Viceroy's dreams of Spanish towns along Ochuse are his alone. When God grants me safe passage back to Spain I can sell the Aztec bowl for enough silver to purchase my own ships! The next time I come to Mexico it will be as a conqueror and plunderer, and the wealth of this land will be mine alone! I have it hidden in my cabin beneath my trunk.

August 18th, 1559, off the shore of Ochuse

We put more colonists ashore today, one boat at a time, with their horses and food. And glad they were to go, too. This voyage is damned, certainly!

God has abandoned us because we are too far from home, too far from Rome and the protection of the Holy Church! Goats and chickens have been found on all the ships, brutally slaughtered. Bloody corpses of slaves are found every morning with their hearts ripped out.

There are rumors of Devils among the crew and beasts coming up over the side like serpents in the darkness. An old Tlaxcalan woman's eyes pierce my soul whenever I pass her in the hold. I sleep with my pistols in hand.

Today a black slave didn't get to his feet when I ordered it so I ran him through. They glared at me wide eyed as I dragged the corpse below decks, but they don't understand.

In my cabin I laid the dead man on top of the idol to bleed into the bowl. I broke it out of the crate days ago and keep it in the center of the room.

Coutzlatl they called it, the Forbidden God! It is beautiful. At night I dream of it!

September 15th, 1559, location unknown

Coutzlatl speaks to me every day, now. I have not heard God in weeks. Does one block the others' words, or are they one in the same? The ship is all but abandoned, and the other ships have been gone for days. We float now with heavy weather approaching.

The stench of rotting corpses sickened me at first, but now I drink it in. They are stacked in the corridor and on the deck, their hearts heaped in Coutzlatl's bowl, buzzing with flies and cockroaches. The old Tlaxcalan woman eludes me, though. She is a medicine woman of some kind, or so one of her kind blurted out when pleading for his life. She cannot escape me for long!

The seas are heaving, and the sails are shredded. The timbers creak as the waves crash over the deck. We're taking on water. Coutzlatl forgive me!

Ladies and Gentleman, Prepare Once Again to be Amazed!

The Twelfth Wonder of the World

(making this the fourth from Salt Lake City's own Professor McClellan!)

Professor McClellan's Electric Stage

Meet me at the Douglas Saloon, 12:30 sharp.
Prof. McClellan

From Salt Lake City to Ackensack in an astounding 6 hours!

Just $1.00!

No nasty teamsters spitting chaw everywhere!

No smelly horses with unsightly dangling privates! Why?

Because it runs on electricity!

Comfortable. Fast. Cheap. Odor Free!

Stages leaving twice daily!

Limited Seating Available!

You will be Amazed!